Beyond the Blues

A Family's Guide
to Postpartum Mood Disorders

SIXTH EDITION

Juliana K. Nason, MA, LMHC, NCC, CMHS, HBCE,
Patricia Spach, MN, ARNP and
Anna Gruen, MSW

ISBN: 0615396712

Acknowledgements

This booklet is dedicated to all of the mothers and families whose lives have been affected by a Postpartum Mood Disorder, and who have taken the courageous steps to reach out to begin the process of healing. Witnessing your courage brings hope and light not only to your own families, but to others whom you touch as well.

We would also like to extend a huge, warm, and heartfelt thanks to all of our talented and dedicated volunteers at Postpartum Support International of Washington (PSI of WA), without whom this very organization would not exist. Your enduring efforts to support postpartum families are admirable and inspiring.

And a sincere thank you to all of our family and friends who spent countless, selfless hours offering help with editing—and re-editing—this text to help ready it for publication.

This booklet is the 6th edition of Beyond the Birth, and we would like to acknowledge the outstanding contributions to the prior editions made by Dawn Gruen, MSW, Rex Gentry, MD, Abigail Myers, ARNP, and Sandra Jolley, PhD, ARNP.

Sales of this booklet help fund community education efforts, as well as contribute to the Dawn Gruen Scholarship Fund. These funds enable families in financial need to receive counseling and support for Postpartum Mood Disorders.

To order more booklets please visit the web site for Postpartum Support International of Washington, www.ppmdsupport.com, where you will find information on pricing for single copies, as well as bulk purchases. You may order online via PayPal at our web site, or send a check, payable to PSI of WA, mailed to:

Postpartum Support International of Washington (PSI of WA)
PO Box 15535
Seattle, WA 98115

For more information, call 888.404.PPMD (7763) or send e-mail to: payment@ppmdsupport.com.

First Edition, Fall 1997	Fourth Edition, Winter 2001
Second Edition, Winter 1997	Fifth Edition, Spring 2003
Third Edition, Winter 1999	Sixth Edition, Spring 2010

Table of Contents

Postpartum Support International of Washington Mission Statement

Our mission is to overcome the effects of Postpartum Mood Disorders through early identification and treatment, thereby ensuring a healthy environment in which mother, baby and family can thrive together.

Postpartum Support International Motto

 Every mother needs a mother.

 If a mother is not well, her family is not well.

 Mothers deserve care and are worthy of being the focus of society's attention.

About Postpartum Support International of Washington

Postpartum Support International of Washington (PSI of WA), formerly known as Depression After Delivery of Washington, is a non-profit organization established in 1987 by Dawn Gruen, ACSW and Lisa Bishop. PSI of WA was designed to support and educate women, families, and professionals about Postpartum Mood Disorders (PPMD). PSI of WA is one of the longest-running postpartum support chapters in the country, thanks to the hard work and dedication of its volunteers.

PSI of WA provides opportunities for women who have experienced and recovered from a Postpartum Mood Disorder to volunteer to help other mothers struggling with PPMD. Over the years, we have provided Warm Line phone support for mothers, drop-in support groups, and educational materials. We have also held conferences to increase awareness, provide education, and further understanding of treatment options among the professional community.

PSI of WA is powered by caring and dedicated volunteers. Our Warm Line and affiliated support group services are offered free of charge. Donations are greatly needed, gladly accepted, and always appreciated. Please contact 888.404.PPMD for more information.

Introduction

The intention of this booklet is to shed light on the experience of those with Postpartum Mood Disorders, an experience that is shared by many new mothers and families after the birth of a baby—but also one that people rarely talk about. Although this booklet primarily focuses on Postpartum Mood Disorders, it can also serve as an important resource for pregnant women who may be in the earliest stages of a Mood Disorder, or who may be at risk for a Postpartum Mood Disorder. Because a Mood Disorder that occurs during pregnancy increases risk for developing a Postpartum Mood Disorder, it is important for women to be assessed during, if not before, pregnancy. It is our greatest hope that no mother suffers in silence, blames herself, or delays treatment because she is too ashamed to come forward. Through this booklet, we aim to extend compassion, alleviate suffering, and to educate mothers and families about treatment options for Postpartum Mood Disorders, whether a Mood Disorder occurs with the first or with subsequent children. It is also our hope that this booklet will provide the knowledge and education to help prevent Postpartum Mood Disorders in expectant mothers.

Beyond the Birth

For nine months you anticipate the birth of your child. As you plan and prepare, you dream of a cozy, warm beginning with your new baby. You feel excited to meet the child that has been your constant companion these past several months—the one whose kicks and rolls have touched your heart with wonder and amazement. Most of your focus has centered on preparing for the birth, and though you know the months to follow will bring changes, you envision this will be a time filled with love, tender moments, and joy.

The nursery is ready, you have completed childbirth preparation classes, and though you are nervous about labor and the birth, you also feel prepared, excited, and in control. Then, a beautiful but completely helpless little person comes into your life. And what can happen next may catch many new mothers and families by surprise.

In the weeks and months following the birth, you might feel emotions you never anticipated. The love for your baby, and the feeling of being so needed, can be very intense. The sense of responsibility can suddenly seem enormous. Caring for this vulnerable little baby might also feel overwhelming at times, especially after days on end of sleeping in two hour stretches, or after your baby has cried inconsolably for hours. Your mind may swim with questions, doubts, and concerns. "What do I do now? Is this what it is going to be like from now on? Am I really prepared to be a parent? Why didn't anyone ever tell us how hard this would be? Can I handle this?"

Normal Emotional Transitions

Giving birth and becoming a mother are wonderful and life changing experiences. Virtually no mother, however, sails through the postpartum period with ease. For all women, the postpartum period is a time of tremendous adjustment, and for some it is quite difficult. Many women feel caught off guard by this adjustment, especially if they begin motherhood with unrealistic views and notions, as many of us do. Indeed, some mothers imagine the days and months after birth to be a magical time filled with golden moments of love. The media contributes to this myth by depicting images of new moms and babies that fail to honestly portray the more difficult aspects of motherhood. With perfectly coiffed hair, slim figures, beautiful makeup, and stylish clothes, these well-rested mothers in their sunny houses make motherhood look so simple; and their smiling, shiny, and always-happy babies add to that image.

There are, in fact, many golden moments, but there are also difficult moments associated with caring for a baby as well. The reality is that taking care of a newborn can be an exhausting job, and one that you are on duty for 24 hours a day, every day, with no breaks, vacations, or pay. Sleep can feel like a distant dream, showering may seem like a luxury, and breast-feeding does not always come easy. If your baby cries a lot, constantly trying to soothe her may feel overwhelming and stressful. And all of this happens while you are trying to adjust not only to your new role as a mother, but also to the changes in your relationship with your spouse or partner as you transition from being a couple to becoming parents. Your self-esteem may be fragile because your body has dramatically changed, you are no longer working, or because you suddenly feel unable to be the competent person you felt you were before your baby was born.

> **"The emotional intensity of the highs and lows that I experienced made me feel as if I was visiting the Mad Hatter's Tea Party,"** said Vanessa, a very organized teacher who loved children and waited years for this well-planned-for child. **"I didn't know who I was anymore. My mind felt full of mush and I knew my body would never look the way it used to. I felt as if I'd lost myself and had made a terrible mistake. I wanted my old life back."**

What Vanessa didn't know at the time was that her feelings were very common. Indeed, many new mothers feel these and other feelings in the months following birth. It is very normal for new mothers to feel vulnerable and yearn to be protected and cared for, especially during the first few months postpartum. Other women feel anxious and out of control because their mood is high or low, or because they cannot control when they sleep, when they eat, or when (and how much) the baby is going to cry. Still other moms feel ambivalent about this new role, and though they love their baby, they do not love the loss of freedom and the changes to their self-image. All of these feelings are normal emotional responses among new mothers. "If someone would have warned me or told me I might feel this way, I might have been better able to handle it. I thought I was the only one who felt this way. I felt there was a 'secret collusion' to not let new parents know how dramatic the changes would be," commented Vanessa.

Many new mothers believe something is wrong with them if they feel this way and are ashamed by these thoughts. The notion that a mother should naturally and instinctually know how to care for her baby, and the idea that she should love every aspect of parenting, further compounds her shame, especially if she lacks confidence in this role or if there are aspects of the role that she dislikes. Sometimes new mothers compare themselves to an imagined "ideal mother" and feel incompetent and somehow flawed by comparison. Also, if the birth experience was not what she had hoped for (for example, an emergency cesarean section instead of a desired "natural" birth), she may believe she failed in some way. These views only add to her guilt and shame, and might prevent her from sharing her feelings with the people closest to her.

During the early postpartum period, sensory connections between the baby and mother are heightened, and though this facilitates maternal-infant bonding, it can also add to a woman's overall sensitivity. Many new mothers feel hypersensitive to stimulation such as noise and activity and can feel more easily overwhelmed, especially when they are sleep deprived or when the baby cries. Other women experience enhanced emotional sensitivity when interacting with their spouse or partner; for example, once previously harmless teasing, criticism, suggestions, or even compliments, can now prompt a rush of emotions, feelings of self-doubt, or uncharacteristic reactions.

Caring for a newborn is not always easy. It is normal to feel anxious and lack confidence in this role. If the baby does not respond as the mother expects, or if the baby is especially difficult to soothe, the mother might worry or conclude that she is not meeting her baby's needs. She might also believe that her baby will be negatively affected if she is not "perfect" in all her parenting. Remember, parenting a newborn is a new role, and as with any new role, it takes time and a bit of trial and error to learn how to best respond to a newborn's needs. Also remember, mothers do not have to be perfect in order to be excellent mothers.

A new baby changes the family dynamics. If a couple has always evenly divided household chores and decision-making, adding a newborn to the mix can disrupt this balance. If there is a stay-at-home parent, she (or he) may feel the need to be the one in charge and responsible for soothing and caring for the baby, and may prevent the other parent from learning their own style of caring for the baby. This can elicit jealousy or rivalry between the parents, with the baby caught in the middle. In addition, sometimes the parent staying at home feels responsible to "do it all." She may try to meet the demands of caring for an infant while also trying to keep up with all the household tasks. If expectations are unrealistic and the chores begin to pile up, the mother may feel overwhelmed and resentful toward her partner. She might also feel guilty and as if she has failed for what she perceives to be her "inability to keep up."

Jan and David were a close couple who felt they had always had good communication between them. When the baby came, neither was ready for the dramatic changes and upheaval in their relationship. David felt insecure and that nothing he did was right. He started working more hours to avoid going home. Jan felt burdened by all the responsibilities and work. She viewed David as acting like a spoiled child, just thinking about himself and his needs. Resentment grew and talking stopped. Only when they were able to confront their fears of being excluded from one another and develop an ability to work as a team, even laugh and cry together about the changes, could they reconcile their differences.

Couples should know that it is normal to have a period of relationship adjustment after the arrival of a new baby. A baby, no matter how wanted, can add considerable stress to a marriage. Sheer exhaustion and

9

the demands of caring for a newborn might make it tempting to shelve difficult discussions and ignore problems, but this approach should be avoided as it can unintentionally lead to resentments developing between a couple. Over time, each partner may withdraw from the other and marriages can suffer. Open communication is essential for couples and families during this time of transition.

Men also undergo changes as they adjust to becoming a new parent. The time that you may have once lavished on your partner is now directed elsewhere, and, in some cases, the new arrival may seem like competition for your precious attention. Men must also navigate the adjustment from your relationship as a couple to becoming a family, and there is little help in showing fathers how to map these uncharted waters. This time, while challenging, presents an opportunity for growth and learning as you become comfortable with your new roles. Both of you should know that this period of adjustment is completely normal and takes time to move through.

Changes to your social support also occur after having a baby. Isolation and stress are two of the most common concerns for new parents. After what may have been years in the workplace with daily adult contact and recognition, not to mention a paycheck, staying home alone with a baby can be one of the most dramatic changes you face. Mothers who had jobs or careers and then decide to stay home with their children may find that they have lost a sense of their identity, and even their competence, during the transition to parenthood.

Past generations handled the demands of caring for an infant with the help of extended family, friends, and community. We now live in a society where most women work, neighbors often keep to themselves, and family members frequently live far apart. The social support mothers once relied on is often not available, leaving many new mothers feeling isolated and alone.

Every new parent needs a strong emotional and practical support system to normalize stressful situations and allow for much-needed breaks. No one should be expected to care for a baby 24 hours a day, seven days a week, without daily periods of time out for oneself.

Jennifer felt that if she took any time for herself, she would somehow be depriving the baby of care, possibly harming him forever. She would hold him throughout the day so that he would sleep, and stay up much of the night to make sure he was okay. Soon she became increasingly fatigued. What Jennifer eventually learned is that by becoming so exhausted she would never have the energy to become the mother she had dreamed of being. When she learned to ask for help, trust the baby would be safe while sleeping, and take care of herself, she eventually had more energy and became the kind of mother she imagined she would be.

Self-care is critical for every new mother. Good self-care means eating balanced and nutritious meals, exercising, learning to ask for help, establishing good boundaries, knowing your own personal limits, and resting and taking breaks. The old saying "you can't give from an empty cup" is all too true. Practicing good self-care is the only way to refill that cup so that you can be present and available for your baby as well as yourself and your family. Put simply, you must take good care of yourself so you can take good care of your baby. Your baby needs you to be healthy, rested, and connected.

In other parts of the world, a birth is seen as a major life change that is honored by certain rituals and structure. Anthropologists suggest that some Western practices unintentionally increase postpartum difficulties because we do not give birthing the importance it deserves. Furthermore, in Western culture, we celebrate the birth of the new baby and tend to ignore the "birth" of the new mother and new family.

Anthropologists have isolated three primary ways that other cultures honor this stage of life:

1. **The postpartum period is given a specific time structure to help new parents adapt.**

   In China, all new mothers and babies receive total physical care for one month, a process they refer to as "doing the month." Mothers are required to rest and food is brought to them. In Malaysia and

Indonesia, they celebrate a 40 day postpartum period, and during this time they perform many rituals connected with the mother's reintegration into society, all the while taking special care to restore her health and beauty. The mother's midwife visits her daily, giving her full-body massages, therapeutic baths, and healing herbs.

2. **The social recognition of the role transition is honored.**

   In the Philippines and in many Latin American countries, new parents are assigned mandated rest and social seclusion to help with the vulnerability and hypersensitivity that comes with being new parents. These cultures honor the mother and give her the necessary time and space to care for her baby, learn the art of breastfeeding, and fully allow her body to recover.

3. **Instrumental assistance to new families is given as a part of the transition to parenthood.**

   Many new mothers need help with instrumental tasks such as cooking or cleaning. In Guatemala, nursing mothers participate in a washing ritual, which acknowledges that breastfeeding can be difficult and that new mothers may need assistance. Mothers are also helped with cooking and cleaning.

In contrast with the nurturing postpartum environment in other cultures, women in the United States have a brief hospitalization after giving birth, and then are expected to be self-sufficient within days, leaving many mothers feeling insecure and overwhelmed. Once home, mothers are often expected to bounce back to a normal routine: making dinner, carrying out household chores, and accommodating swarms of visitors. In our culture, help with meals or with the laundry used to be provided by other family members, but today, many new mothers no longer live near their own mothers, or their extended families are not available to help. This means mothers may need to ask for help, and this can feel awkward or like a sign of weakness. With so many expectations placed on mothers, we often fail to give them the rest needed to nurture and bond with their newborn. Mothering is a learning process, each baby is unique, and the dance of attachment and attunement takes time.

So, how do you know when normal postpartum adjustments become problematic? Most new parents have heard about the Baby Blues, but know very little about other, more serious mood problems. The following few sections outline the symptoms of the Baby Blues, as well as the symptoms of other Postpartum Mood Disorders. The Baby Blues usually does not require treatment, but specialized treatment—beyond that of simple physical care and support—is usually indicated if you have one of the Mood Disorders listed below. This is particularly true if you have been diagnosed with or if you think you might have Bipolar Disorder.

The Baby Blues

The Baby Blues is the most well known of all postpartum mood adjustments. Within the first three to five days after delivery, up to 80 percent of new mothers can experience temporary emotional distress. This is not considered a Postpartum Mood Disorder, as it tends to resolve spontaneously within a few weeks. These mood changes may in part be due to the rapid hormonal changes taking place after delivery, insufficient sleep, emotional exhaustion, and the stresses of becoming a new mother. These symptoms typically last through the first two weeks postpartum.

Symptoms of the Baby Blues include:
- Decreased appetite
- Lack of sleep
- Lack of energy
- Irritability
- Oversensitivity
- Sadness
- Crying
- Lack of confidence
- Low self-esteem
- Feeling stressed or overwhelmed

With adequate sleep, good nutrition, and strong emotional and practical support these symptoms should resolve completely within two weeks.

If after two or three weeks postpartum these symptoms continue or increase, it may indicate a more serious problem, and you should inform your health care provider as soon as possible.

Postpartum Mood Disorders

A Postpartum Mood Disorder can develop in any new parent, including mothers, fathers, and adoptive parents. Please note that statistics given below are for biological mothers in the postpartum period. Postpartum Mood Disorders can also develop in mothers who recently terminated a pregnancy, lost a baby through miscarriage, and in mothers/fathers who experienced any other neonatal loss such as a stillbirth. Symptoms can begin any time in the first 15 months following the birth of a baby. Sometimes symptoms of a Postpartum Mood Disorder arise at key hormonal shifts during that first year and a half, such as when a mother's menses return or during the weaning of her baby. It should again be noted that symptoms of Anxiety, Depression, and other Mood Disorders often develop in pregnancy, and are risk factors for Mood Disorders in the postpartum period.

Research on Postpartum Mood Disorders has revealed several types of postpartum psychiatric illness. In the popular media, the term "Postpartum Depression" is often wrongly used as an umbrella term for all postpartum psychiatric conditions. This is incorrect, for we know there are many and varied symptoms among the Postpartum Mood Disorders. The following will clarify these distinctions and enable mothers and fathers to better understand their symptoms and name them more accurately. It is important to remember that a woman can experience overlapping symptoms and that different Postpartum Mood Disorders often co-occur. For example, one person can have symptoms of Depression, along with symptoms of Anxiety with or without Panic Attacks, and can also have some obsessive thoughts. Treatment in this case would focus on alleviating multiple symptoms.

Postpartum Depression

Clinical Depression affects every aspect of a person's life—mind, body, and spirit. Research estimates reveal that in the United States, each year approximately 19 million people (or 1 in 10 adults) experience Depression, and that nearly two-thirds do not get the help they need.

Depression is an illness that affects both women and men, but women experience Depression at roughly twice the rate of men. Researchers continue to explore how the special biological and psychosocial circumstances unique to women may be associated with their higher rate of Depression. It should be noted that at no time in a woman's life cycle is she more vulnerable to Depression than in her childbearing years.

Prevalence of Major Depression by Gender

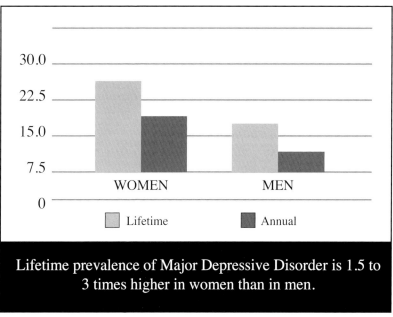

Lifetime prevalence of Major Depressive Disorder is 1.5 to 3 times higher in women than in men.

Kessler, R.C. et al. (1994). Lifetime and 12-month prevalence of DSM-III-R psychiatric disorders in the United States. Results from the National Comorbidity Survey. Archives of General Psychiatry, Jan, 51(1): 8-19.

Estimated Prevalence of Perinatal Depression

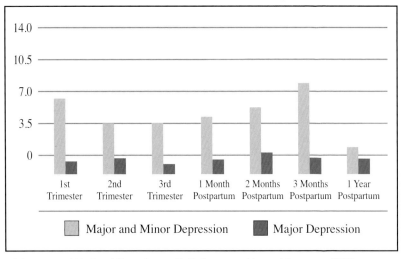

U.S. Department of Health and Human Services, Health Resources and Services Administration (2005). Women's Health USA 2005. Rockville, Maryland: U.S. Department of Health and Human Services.

Postpartum Depression affects up to 15 percent of new mothers, and can have a profound and lasting impact on mothers, babies, and families. The most common symptoms of Postpartum Depression are outlined below. As you can see, postpartum depressive symptoms share many symptoms in common with the previously described Baby Blues. The main difference is that the Baby Blues resolves spontaneously in two or three weeks, whereas Postpartum Depression persists and intensifies, and typically does not resolve without intervention. A diagnosis of Postpartum Depression may be difficult for the untrained provider because many of the physical symptoms of Major Depression such as changes in sleep, appetite, lack of energy, and fatigue are common in both the normal postpartum period and in Postpartum Depression. You may have some but not all of these symptoms. If you have any questions about what you are experiencing, you should seek help from a qualified provider.

Symptoms of Postpartum Depression include:

- Depressed mood
- Lack of energy
- Mental confusion
- Frequent crying
- Low self-esteem
- Feelings of guilt or shame
- Feelings of worthlessness
- Irritability or anger
- Feeling overwhelmed
- Forgetfulness
- Diminished or absent sex drive
- Anxiety
- Feelings of hopelessness
- Sleep difficulties (sleeping too much or too little)
- Eating issues (eating too much or too little)
- Suicidal thoughts

Typically symptoms must be present every day for at least two weeks, and significantly interfere with one's daily life and functioning. You do not have to have all of these symptoms to meet the diagnostic criteria for Postpartum Depression, but usually mothers report experiencing many of them.

It is important that women with Postpartum Depression seek treatment early in the course of the illness from a qualified provider. Postpartum Depression, if left untreated, can interfere with your ability to enjoy parenting your baby and hinder attachment and bonding. This can have long-term negative consequences for your child if not addressed promptly. In addition, Postpartum Depression can disrupt your relationship with your spouse and other family members. Depression can also interfere with your ability to work or otherwise carry out the tasks of everyday life. Left untreated, some women with Postpartum Depression may turn to drugs and alcohol as a way of "self-medicating" their symptoms. In severe cases of Postpartum Depression, some women contemplate self-harm or suicide as a way to escape their symptoms. If you are having thoughts of self-harm or suicide, you should seek help *immediately*. You can start by telling your medical provider, who can help you find a psychiatrist, psychiatric nurse practitioner, and/or licensed therapist specializing in the treatment of women with Postpartum Depression. If you don't feel comfortable confiding in your provider, call the PSI of WA Warm Line, tell a friend, your spouse, or anyone else whom you trust.

Postpartum Anxiety

Like Postpartum Depression, Postpartum Anxiety symptoms can begin anytime within the first 15 months of giving birth. Postpartum Anxiety is frequently, but not always, experienced by mothers who also have symptoms of Depression. Postpartum Anxiety Disorders can affect up to 10 percent of new mothers.

Symptoms of Postpartum Anxiety include:

- Excessive worry or concern that is difficult to control (often presenting as excessive concern over the health and safety of the baby)
- Feeling restless or on edge
- Being easily fatigued
- Difficulty concentrating
- Irritability
- Muscle tension
- Sleep disturbance

Postpartum Panic Disorder

Postpartum Panic Disorder is a specific type of Anxiety Disorder. Symptoms of a Panic Attack, often confused with those of a heart attack, leave many mothers traveling from doctor to doctor searching for a physical cause of their symptoms. Of course, before a patient is treated for a Panic Disorder, medical causes for their symptoms should be ruled out. Once a person has experienced a Panic Attack, they may fear having another one. This fear can lead to a terrible cycle of anxiety, panic, and avoidance of any places or triggers the mother believes will lead to another Panic Attack. Sometimes mothers develop Agoraphobia (fear or avoidance of going to places where they might panic and cannot escape) in response to Panic Attacks. Postpartum Panic Disorder can affect up to 10 percent of new mothers. If you have had any of these symptoms, please seek help from a qualified provider who can help sort out your symptoms and rule out any underlying physical causes.

Symptoms of Postpartum Panic Disorder include:

- Anxiety symptoms (listed under Postpartum Anxiety, above)
- Shortness of breath
- Choking or smothering sensations
- Heart palpitations or racing heartbeat
- Chest pains or discomfort
- Dizziness, lightheadedness, or feelings of unsteadiness
- Sweating or sweaty palms
- Faintness
- Nausea or abdominal distress
- Hot flashes or chills
- Shaking or trembling
- Numbness or tingling sensations, especially in hands
- Depersonalization
  (feeling disoriented or that the world has become unreal)
- Feelings of intense dread
- Fear of being out of control or going crazy
- Fear that you are dying

Postpartum Obsessive-Compulsive Disorder (OCD)

Postpartum Obsessive-Compulsive Disorder is a type of Postpartum Anxiety Disorder characterized by obsessive thoughts, and manifested by compulsive rituals. There are no clear statistics on how many women experience Obsessive-Compulsive Disorders during the postpartum period, since obsessions and compulsions can appear separately or can co-occur with Depression, and/or Panic Disorder. Roughly 3 to 5 percent of new mothers experience this condition.

As the name implies, Postpartum Obsessive-Compulsive Disorder is characterized by obsessions and compulsions. **Obsessions** are recurrent, intrusive, and often inappropriate thoughts that cannot be controlled. They cause extreme anxiety and distress, mostly because they seem so inappropriate or do not make sense. The new mother will keep thinking about a certain thought or repeating an action over and over, and she may find it hard to get the thoughts out of her mind or stop the resulting behaviors.

It is important to note that at some point the mother will recognize that the obsessive thoughts, impulses or images are a product of her own mind, and that the obsessions and compulsions are unreasonable or excessive. Typically, mothers attempt to get rid of these impulses or images or to neutralize them with another thought or action.

Compulsions are behaviors that women perform to lessen the anxiety or discomfort that arises from obsessions. Compulsions typically include repetitive, purposeful, intentional behaviors called rituals. While rituals are practiced to reduce anxiety from obsessions, the behavior is typically done to excess. Some examples are:

- Washing and cleaning rituals, which reduce concerns about contamination
- Avoiding dangerous objects (such as knives), which reduces anxiety about harm or aggression
- Checking the baby obsessively to see if he is still breathing, or checking locks on doors and windows excessively, which reduces fears of safety or intrusion
- Straightening and arranging items, which reduces discomfort resulting from disorder
- Hoarding items, which counteracts fears of losing or being without things of importance or value

Obsessive thoughts often lead to compulsive checking behaviors, where the mother feels compelled to frequently check on her baby because she fears that something bad will happen if she doesn't. Other obsessive thoughts and compulsive behaviors seen in mothers with Postpartum Obsessive-Compulsive Disorder involve obsessive fears of either harming or having harm come to the baby. Some examples of these "scary thoughts" are:

- The baby's bottles will somehow become contaminated (often resulting in compulsively sterilizing the bottles)
- Drowning the baby (especially in the bath)
- Putting the baby in the microwave
- Stabbing the baby
- Throwing the baby in the garbage
- Throwing the baby down the stairs or over a tall railing

Obsessive thinking in the postpartum period may have some neurobiological connections, such as an imbalance of hormones and brain chemicals, like oxytocin. Obsessive thinking may also stem from a need and drive to be a perfect parent or to provide a perfect environment for the baby, and the fear of not being able to do so. Most research, however, has failed to fully explain the causes of Postpartum Obsessive-Compulsive Disorder, but as with all psychiatric illnesses, mothers should not blame themselves for their symptoms, and they should know that this condition is very treatable.

Symptoms of Postpartum Obsessive-Compulsive Disorder include:

Obsessions as defined by:

Recurrent and persistent thoughts, impulses, or images that are experienced, at some time during the disturbance, as intrusive and inappropriate, and that cause marked anxiety or distress.

The thoughts, impulses, or images are not simply excessive worries about real-life problems.

The person attempts to ignore or suppress such thoughts, impulses, or images, or to neutralize them with some other thought or action.

The person recognizes that the obsessive thoughts, impulses, or images are a product of his or her own mind (not imposed from outside of oneself as in thought insertion—the belief that someone else is putting the thought into your head).

Compulsions as defined by:

Repetitive behaviors or mental acts that the person feels driven to perform in response to an obsession, or according to rules that must be rigidly applied.

The behaviors or mental acts are aimed at preventing or reducing distress or preventing some dreaded event or situation. However, these behaviors or mental acts are either not connected in a realistic way with what they are designed to neutralize or prevent, or are clearly excessive.

At some point during the course of the disorder, the person has recognized that the obsessions or compulsions are excessive or unreasonable. The obsessions or compulsions cause marked distress, are time consuming (take more than 1 hour a day), or significantly interfere with the person's normal routine or other daily functioning.

Scary or intrusive thoughts

Scary or intrusive thoughts, as described above, commonly occur in women with Postpartum Obsessive-Compulsive Disorder. These could include thoughts that you might hurt your baby or that something horrible might happen to her such as: "my baby might fall out of the window;" "if I bathe him he will drown;" "there is something seriously wrong with her;" or "he'd be better off without me." As discussed above, these thoughts are often accompanied by specific actions, such as getting rid of all of the knives in the house in order to protect the baby from harm, and are frequently reported by many mothers with this disorder. Normally, a woman will recognize that these thoughts are disturbing and alien to her, and that they are not real. She knows these thoughts are not ones she wishes to act on, and is often scared and ashamed that she is even having the thoughts in the first place, not to mention that she can't seem to make them go away.

If a mother believes in her intrusive thoughts, or if she believes someone outside of her is telling her to do things, then she may be experiencing psychotic symptoms. *This distinction between believing her thoughts and knowing that they are products of her illness is a crucial one.* A mother with Postpartum Obsessive-Compulsive Disorder knows that her thoughts are wrong and *does not* want to hurt her baby, yet the thoughts continue. A mother with Postpartum Psychosis (discussed below) believes that her thoughts are appropriate or logical, and is at risk of acting on them.

A mother with these symptoms should be encouraged to share her thoughts so her family and provider can find out how invested she is in believing them. If she hides these thoughts because she is ashamed or fears rejection and criticism, or if her thoughts are minimized, she may feel incredibly isolated and beyond help, and her desperation may increase. Whether these thoughts are obsessive symptoms, or symptoms of Psychosis, it is important to know that they are both treatable conditions.

A knowledgeable provider can help differentiate between the two types of thoughts and can reassure the mother with Postpartum Obsessive-Compulsive Disorder, and her family, that she is not "crazy" and that these are very treatable symptoms of a Postpartum Anxiety Disorder.

If she does believe them (as in the case of a delusion), then she is likely experiencing Psychosis, and *must be evaluated immediately,* as this is considered to be a psychiatric emergency. In cases of Postpartum Psychosis, the mother will most likely need to be hospitalized to be stabilized and to ensure the safety of herself and the baby. She will need to be cared for after her hospitalization by a psychiatrist or psychiatric nurse practitioner, and a licensed therapist trained in the treatment of Postpartum Mood Disorders.

Examples of obsessive and psychotic symptoms

Obsessive symptoms:

Kathy had given birth to her second child, a girl. At two months postpartum, she began to feel anxious and worry that she was crazy. She had read about the Texas tragedy involving a woman who drowned all five of her children during the postpartum period of her fifth birth. Kathy became obsessed with the thought that she might suddenly "turn into that Texas woman." This thought would pop into her mind several times a day, especially when she was alone or not otherwise distracted. She revealed these thoughts to her provider and stated they frightened her, but that she knew these thoughts were "crazy." She was reassured these symptoms and thoughts would eventually go away with appropriate therapy and an antidepressant medication. Her anxiety was greatly diminished each time she was reassured. Eventually these thoughts went away entirely.

Psychotic symptoms:

Amy began saying to her husband four days after giving birth that she "just knew" that her baby had a brain tumor, and that no one was telling her the truth about the baby's health. Despite reassurances that all tests on the baby were negative, Amy could not be otherwise convinced by either her family or her care providers. She began to lie awake all night and to stare off into space many times during the day. A couple of days later, Amy's husband came into the bedroom just in time to find Amy holding a pillow over her baby's head to "put him out of the misery he is going through." Amy was hospitalized, treated with an antipsychotic medication and a mood stabilizer, and became well and functional in a few weeks. A near-tragedy had been averted.

In the above example, it is important to note that the act of holding the pillow over the baby's head is not what constitutes a psychotic symptom. It is the *belief* that her baby would be better off dead, along with her actions, which together constitute the diagnosis of Psychosis. Many mothers with obsessive symptoms have the thought or intrusive image of holding a pillow over their baby's head, but they are not going to act on it because they are so frightened by the thought that they go to great lengths to protect the baby. They often think they are so potentially dangerous that the baby would be better off without their mother around. If you are feeling this way, please reach out for help today—tell your spouse, a close friend, or someone else you trust, but do not suffer alone in silence. This is a treatable condition, one that you can overcome. You can be well again with the proper help, including skilled medical and therapeutic care.

Posttraumatic Stress Disorder (PTSD)

Posttraumatic Stress Disorder (PTSD) can occur when something perceived to be traumatic, frightening, or life threatening is either experienced or witnessed by the mother. Posttraumatic Stress Disorder, that occurs as a result of a traumatic birth experience, has only recently been recognized, and may affect roughly 6 percent of new mothers. The traumatic event could happen any time during the pregnancy, labor, delivery, or the postpartum period. Symptoms might appear soon after birth or may emerge later, but usually develop within the first six months postpartum. If left untreated, some women may get better within about two years. For others, untreated trauma can result in chronic symptoms and distress.

What constitutes birth related "trauma" is highly subjective and not every woman is traumatized by the same events; indeed, many women exposed to "traumatic" events experience no PTSD at all. Some women however, may feel traumatized by events such as managed or induced labor, poor pain relief, feelings of loss of control, impersonal treatment by medical staff, lack of attention or dignity during labor, invasive procedures, or an unexpected Cesarean Section. Others feel traumatized if there was an obstetric emergency, medical complications that resulted in the baby being admitted to the Neonatal Intensive Care Unit (NICU), unmet needs to debrief or process the birth experience, or the woman sustained an injury as a result of the birth. These and other birth experiences can also activate existing traumatic memories in women with a history of sexual abuse or other past trauma, and can lead to intrusive memories, distress from re-experiencing the prior traumatic event, anger, and other symptoms of PTSD.

Symptoms of Posttraumatic Stress Disorder include:

- Experience of an event that was perceived by the individual as traumatic
- Flashbacks or sudden intrusive memories of the event
- Nightmares
- Exaggerated startle response ("edginess")
- Hyperarousal (always being "on guard")
- Hypervigilance (constantly monitoring for stressors or looming trouble)
- Intense physiological distress (such as Panic Attacks, sweating, nausea) upon exposure to events similar to the traumatic event
- Inability to recall important aspects of the traumatic event
- Avoidance of reminders of the traumatic event
- Anger or rage
- Fantasies of retaliation
- Cynicism or distrust
- Foreshortened sense of the future
- Hypersensitivity to injustice
- Anxiety
- Depression

Bipolar Disorder with postpartum onset

Bipolar Disorder occurs in roughly 2.6 percent of the general population. The postpartum period represents an especially vulnerable time for women with a history of Bipolar Disorder. In addition, a woman with no prior history of Bipolar Disorder can have her first mood episode of Bipolar Disorder during the postpartum period. There are two main types of Bipolar Disorder: Bipolar I and Bipolar II. Some experts, however, believe Bipolar Disorder actually exists on a spectrum.

Bipolar I Disorder is characterized by intense mood episodes that include at least one episode of Major Depression (see symptom list above) and one episode of Mania (see symptom list below). Bipolar II Disorder is diagnosed when a woman has had at least one Hypomanic episode (a shorter and less intense version of Mania) and at least one episode of Major Depression.

Many individuals with Bipolar II Disorder present with Depression, and most of their mood episodes may be depressive ones. Thus, this type of Bipolar Disorder is often very difficult to diagnose, especially if the woman fails to recognize and report the times when she was a bit manic, because it may just feel like a lifting of Depression, or because these times feel good and they are hard to recognize as Hypomanic. A psychiatrist, psychiatric nurse practitioner, and/or licensed therapist with specialized training in working with Postpartum Mood Disorders should be consulted in order to make an accurate diagnosis.

It is very important for mothers to consider and report their family history, especially if it includes any relatives with Bipolar Disorder. This is important information to share with your provider because it may help them accurately diagnose your Mood Disorder. Indeed, some women who initially present with Postpartum Depression actually have a Bipolar Disorder and are suffering from Bipolar Depression. It is estimated that between 25 to 45 percent of women who present with symptoms of Postpartum Depression actually meet criteria for a Bipolar Disorder. Many mothers report periods of Hypomania just after the birth of their baby and confuse this with the "elation" of childbirth. This is very important for a qualified provider to sort out, because antidepressants alone are not likely to be helpful in this situation, and, by themselves, can even be harmful to mothers with a Bipolar Spectrum Disorder.

Symptoms of Mania or Hypomania include:

- Changes in mood for a distinct period of time, such as feeling extremely and unusually happy, optimistic, euphoric, or irritable
- Changes in thinking, such as racing thoughts, unrealistic self confidence, difficulty concentrating, grandiose plans, hallucinations* (Mania only) or delusions** (Mania only)
- Changes in behavior, such as increased activity or socializing, immersion in plans or projects, talking very rapidly and excessively, excessive spending, impaired judgment, or impulsive sexual activity
- Changes in physical condition, such as less need for sleep, increased energy, and fewer health complaints

A hallucination is a profound distortion in a person's perception of reality, typically accompanied by a powerful sense of reality. A hallucination may be a sensory experience in which a person can see, hear, smell, taste, or feel something that is not there.

**A delusion is a false personal belief that is not subject to reason or contradictory evidence and is not explained by a person's usual cultural and religious concepts. A delusion may be firmly maintained in the face of incontrovertible evidence that it is false.*

Women with Bipolar Disorder can and do have very successful experiences having children; it is extremely important, however, that mothers who have been diagnosed with this condition are informed of the risks and benefits of treatment. In addition, it is crucial that a knowledgeable psychiatric provider monitor them carefully throughout their pregnancy and during the postpartum period.

Postpartum Psychosis

Psychosis is a condition that occurs in the context of another underlying psychiatric disorder such as Bipolar Disorder or Schizophrenia. Postpartum Psychosis is a very serious but uncommon disorder, affecting 1 or 2 in every 1000 new mothers. For some women, a postpartum psychotic episode may be the only psychotic episode they will ever experience. For others, a postpartum psychotic episode may be the first episode of a chronic psychiatric disorder, or an acute exacerbation of another underlying disorder. Typically, it has an early onset, often within the first few days to two weeks following delivery.

Postpartum Psychosis usually begins with severe insomnia, irritability, rapidly shifting moods (often either Depression or Mania), and overly-active behavior. If well informed, the couple will know what steps to take and whom to call for help. There have been numerous instances of Postpartum Psychosis that the media has mislabeled and portrayed as Postpartum Depression, perpetuating public misinformation and creating fear. This has led to a climate where women are often afraid to speak out about the emotionally uncomfortable or concerning things they might be feeling following the birth of a child. It is important to understand that Postpartum Psychosis is rare, but almost always more severe than Postpartum Depression, and is usually a case of an undiagnosed Bipolar Disorder.

Among all of the cases of Postpartum Psychosis, 4 percent result in suicide and/or infanticide. These tragedies can be prevented if professionals and families know how to recognize a psychotic episode, and the mother then receives appropriate care. It is imperative that we identify those at risk as early as possible, ideally during or before pregnancy. Obstetricians, family doctors, midwives, or nurse practitioners should take a careful history of a woman's family psychiatric history, as well as her own history of Mood Disorders. Women with a past history of a psychotic illness who become pregnant should be monitored closely by an expert, and may need to be maintained on medication during pregnancy.

Postpartum Psychosis is always considered a medical emergency. Researchers are now finding that most of the time, *psychotic episodes in the postpartum period are due to Bipolar Disorder*, and are characterized by periods of normal awareness, alternating with periods where there is loss of touch with reality. Minutes, or hours, can separate these breaks in reality from normal periods of awareness. Initially, the woman may appear highly anxious, but then begin to exhibit delusions (beliefs in her bizarre thoughts). During a psychotic episode, the woman loses touch with reality; she may hallucinate, have delusions, and/or be thought-disordered (her thought process may be illogical or chaotic). Again, this is the most severe Postpartum Mood Disorder and requires *immediate intervention*, which, as stated above, usually requires hospitalization, and must always be treated with medication.

Symptoms of Postpartum Psychosis include:

- Hallucinations
- Delusions
- Disordered thinking
- Sleep disturbances
- Agitation
- Social withdrawal
- Behavioral changes
- Loss of motivation
- Severe and rapid mood swings
- Incoherence
- Blunting of affect or emotions
- Inability to differentiate hallucinations from reality

The presence of insight (awareness of the illness or that something is not right) is usually (but not always) indicative of a non-psychotic illness. Remember, an experienced professional must assess the presence of insight and suicide risk. Because of her confusion, the woman may not have the insight to recognize how ill she is. Therefore, the decision for hospitalization may need to be made by her medical provider.

Three questions that may help determine the mother's level of insight:

What do you think is happening with you/what do you call the problem?

What do you think caused it?

What do you think needs to happen to get you better?

Please consult an expert immediately if you have any fears or concerns that you or your loved one may be developing Postpartum Psychosis.

Risk Factors for Postpartum Mood Disorders

Researchers cannot say for sure what causes Postpartum Mood Disorders, but they have been able to isolate risk factors and describe four primary areas of influence that likely contribute to risk for Postpartum Mood Disorders.

Physiological factors

To date, no research points to any one physiological cause of Postpartum Mood Disorders. Most evidence suggests that the normal physiological changes that occur before pregnancy, during pregnancy, or during the postpartum period influence a woman's neurobiology. For example, some researchers believe that the dramatic drop in cortisol, progesterone and estrogen immediately following birth may contribute to mood changes and thus to the development of Postpartum Mood Disorders. Brain research shows that estrogen acts as a neurotransmitter (a chemical that helps brain cells communicate correctly). Thus, when estrogen levels drop rapidly following birth, less estrogen is available in the brain, leaving some women vulnerable to Depression, Anxiety, and other Mood Disorders. Women with a personal or family history of Depression, Anxiety, or other mental illnesses, are especially susceptible to these changes, and carry a 60 percent increased risk of developing a Postpartum Mood Disorder.

Changes to the brain's stress response system may also play a role in the development of a Postpartum Mood Disorder, and might be influenced by prior exposure to multiple severe stressors (psychological stressors and/or physical stressors). Recent research also shows a correlation between Diabetes, including Gestational Diabetes, and the development of a Postpartum Mood Disorder.

Physiological risk factors for developing a Postpartum Mood Disorder include:

- History of Premenstrual Syndrome
- History of sensitivity to other hormonal shifts (Depression at puberty, after pregnancy loss, in reaction to birth control or fertility treatments)
- History of mental health problems
- History of Postpartum Mood Disorders
- Depression or Anxiety during pregnancy
- Family history of Mood Disorders
- History of Eating Disorders
- Thyroid Disorder or Diabetes (including Gestational Diabetes)

Stress and issues of social support

Lack of social support is a significant risk factor for the development of a Postpartum Mood Disorder. In one of our previous examples, David coped with his feelings of anxiety by working more, which made Jan feel isolated and solely responsible for caring for their baby. Had this situation continued, Jan's feelings would likely have intensified, and her isolation might have made a difficult time of adjustment even worse, putting her at risk for a Postpartum Mood Disorder. It is very important for mothers to feel socially connected, as this protects women from stress in the post-partum period.

Another couple, Jim and Marie, had just moved to a new neighborhood. They had a history of ignoring most of their conflicts and they focused more on their individual interests than on each other. When their baby was born, both felt increasingly isolated and overwhelmed with their new responsibilities. Soon, they begin to resent each other. Jim began having acute physical symptoms, such as headaches and stomach pain. Marie felt increasingly anxious and had bouts of feeling very depressed. Each experienced their own postpartum reaction to the stress of a new baby, but neither understood why they felt the way they did and both blamed the other.

Stress in any form can impact a couple during the postpartum period, and they should make every effort possible to openly communicate, support each other, and get help if they cannot resolve their differences.

Stress can also arise from unresolved loss or grief. The postpartum months are a time when many new mothers want to be nurtured by their own mother. If this relationship is strained or distant, new mothers may grieve this loss. A new parent might also grieve the death of her parent (even though that parent may have died many years before) because this momentous occasion reminds her of their absence. In addition, the memory of a previous miscarriage or termination of pregnancy can activate feelings of loss during this vulnerable time. Some of the other losses women might grapple with include loss of freedom, changes to body image, loss of interest in (or lack of time for) sex, loss of being the focus of attention, decreased time for active friendships, lack of privacy and personal space, loss of career and the self-image that goes with it, and a diminished sense of "couplehood." If a mother minimizes these losses, or perhaps fails to recognize them altogether, she is more likely to develop symptoms of Anxiety or despair.

A baby's temperament can also affect the mother's stress level. For example, when a baby is difficult to soothe, cries a lot, or does not sleep much, parents tend to doubt themselves and assume blame for their baby's distress. This self-doubt can undermine a parent's confidence and produce feelings of anxiety any time the baby awakens. Then a cycle develops where the parent fears that somehow they are not being a good a parent, they feel anxious every time the baby cries, and in turn, their self-doubt increases.

Risk factors for developing a Postpartum Mood Disorder that involve stress and issues of social support:

- Miscarriage or other neonatal loss
- Previous termination of pregnancy
- Past infertility
- Adoption
- Unplanned or unwanted pregnancy
- Ambivalence about the pregnancy
- Birth trauma
- Medical problems with baby or parent
- Challenging infant temperament
- Change in job or loss of career
- Poverty and economic pressures
- Recent move or change in living arrangements
- Recent immigration
- Previous death of close family member
- Separation from parent in childhood
- Marital difficulties
- Current or past abuse of any type
- Poor social support
- Young maternal age
- Single parenting

Interpersonal factors

Interpersonal factors take into consideration the personality and temperament of the parent.

> Michele was always clear and directed about how to achieve her goals. A perfectionist at work and home, she also prided herself on helping others. But, as a new mother, she was a prime candidate for having a difficult adjustment to the lack of control and unpredictability a child brings. She began having Panic Attacks when the baby cried. The expectation that she should know how to parent and her fear of asking for help became distorted. She began having obsessive thoughts that her baby did not like her when she could not comfort him, and began to view herself as a "bad mother."

Interpersonal risk factors for developing a Postpartum Mood Disorder include:

- Negative outlook on the world
- External sense of control
- Overly eager to please others
- Very task oriented
- Rigidity
- Perfectionist tendencies
- Negative expectations of birth or parenting
- Very high expectations of birth or parenting
- Interpretation of the infant's temperament as being the fault of the parent
- Inadequate or ineffective coping skills

Family history factors

How we were parented and our prior life experiences may leave us vulnerable to problems adjusting to parenting.

> **Marian came from a family where substance abuse and physical abuse was the norm. She learned early on that she was not cared about and had few rights in her family. As a child, she coped by escaping any difficult situation through music, reading, and talking to friends. With little self-esteem and no healthy parenting models, Marian had few resources from which to draw. She feared that any frustration or anger that she might feel could cause her to abuse her children. She overcompensated by being overprotective of her baby and would not let anyone else care for him. Marian soon recognized that she needed help to learn constructive ways to cope or she would soon become totally exhausted.**

Family history risk factors for developing a Postpartum Mood Disorder include:

- History of physical, sexual, or emotional abuse
- History of substance abuse
- Poor mother/daughter or father/daughter relationship
- Low self-esteem
- Personal experience of being poorly parented
- Family history of mental illness

Risk Factors for Postpartum Mood Disorders – An Overview

Please note that the following list is not diagnostic, but rather provides an overview of potential vulnerabilities that one may have to developing a Postpartum Mood Disorder. While we don't know the exact cause of Postpartum Mood Disorders, they are likely a combination of biological, hormonal, environmental, and psychological factors. The combination of risk factors will be unique to each individual, their biological make up, and their personal circumstances. It is also possible that some women may have no risk factors at all. Fortunately, while we do not know exactly what causes Postpartum Mood Disorders, we do know what to do to effectively treat them.

Physiological risk factors	History of Premenstrual Syndrome; history of sensitivity to other hormonal shifts (Depression at puberty, after pregnancy loss, in reaction to birth control or fertility treatments); history of mental health problems; history of Postpartum Mood Disorders; Depression or Anxiety during pregnancy; family history of Mood Disorders; history of Eating Disorders; Thyroid Disorder or Diabetes (including Gestational Diabetes)
Risk factors related to stress and issues of social support	Miscarriage or other neonatal loss; previous termination of pregnancy; past infertility; adoption; unplanned or un-wanted pregnancy; ambivalence about the pregnancy; birth trauma; medical problems with baby or parent; challenging infant temperament; change in job or loss of career; poverty and economic pressures; recent move or change in living arrangements; recent immigration; previous death of close family member; separation from parent in childhood; marital difficulties; current or past abuse of any type; poor social support; young maternal age; single parenting
Interpersonal risk factors	Negative outlook on the world; external sense of control; overly eager to please others; very task oriented; rigidity; perfectionist tendencies; negative expectations of birth or parenting; very high expectations of birth or parenting; interpretation of the infant's temperament as being the fault of the parent; inadequate or ineffective coping skills
Family history risk factors	History of physical, sexual, or emotional abuse; history of substance abuse; poor mother/daughter or father/daughter relationship; low self-esteem; personal experience of being poorly parented; family history of mental illness

Women of Color and Low-Income Women's Experiences with Postpartum Mood Disorders

Women living in poverty, as well as women of color, often deal with compromising factors that prevent them from recognizing Postpartum Mood Disorders and accessing treatment at the same rates as Caucasian middle and upper class women do. Many low-income women and women of color may have difficulties recognizing Depression because they more typically view depressive symptoms as naturally occurring emotions that are part of everyday life.

Women of color

Culture can shape how a person perceives an illness of any type, and it therefore affects how they perceive Depression and its treatment. Significant cultural issues to consider related to Postpartum Mood Disorders and women of color include the following:

- Manifestation of symptoms
- Spirituality and views of illness
- Less access to insurance and health care
- Limited culturally competent treatment options
- Limited financial and material resources
- Family and community support
- Verbal and nonverbal communication styles
- Social and cultural stigmas against Depression
- Inadequate language information regarding Depression

Many cultures hold unique beliefs about psychiatric illnesses and express symptoms of these illnesses in culturally-specific ways. Culture also plays a role in how—and if—the woman seeks treatment. Women of color, for example, often put others before themselves and play the role of the nurturer for their family and in their communities. In addition, for some African American mothers, Depression is perceived as a personal weakness, and is not seen as a legitimate health problem. In addition, they might distrust the health care system because of traumatic experiences with it in their past. Thus, they may rely on their friends and religious communities for support, and therefore delay seeking professional treatment.

Asian American women, on the other hand, are more inclined to report the physical symptoms of Depression and therefore seek medical help before mental health care. In addition, in many Asian communities, expression of one's feelings is seen as an admission of weakness. This may prevent these mothers from ever reporting their struggles to friends or family.

For many Native American communities, traditional healing is used by the majority and considered more advisable than care from a physician.

Many Latinas may feel guilt or shame, and fear being considered "crazy." Some may be afraid of jeopardizing their immigration status if they seek help, and may feel apprehensive about the medical field and medications.

Multiple factors may deter women who are immigrants from seeking help, including language and cultural barriers, a history of trauma and PTSD, fear of losing their children, unfamiliarity with a new culture, fear of rejection, and family shame.

Low-income women

Although Postpartum Mood Disorders affect communities across race, ethnicity and socioeconomic background, research has shown that the incidence of Postpartum Depression is highest for women living in poverty, regardless of race or ethnicity. Too often low-income women face difficult life circumstances, such as lack of social support networks, substance abuse, intimate partner violence, childhood abuse, and stressors linked to a life of hardship, all of which impact their ability to recognize and receive treatment for Depression. For women living in poverty, limited options for affordable and accessible health care further restrict their ability to identify and receive treatment, especially on a consistent basis.

Treatment for Postpartum Mood Disorders in low-income women and women of color should emphasize a family approach that involves treating the mother and child in a safe setting, for example, with early childhood programs, like Head Start, and other home visitation programs. This would provide supportive opportunities for parents to learn about Depression, and may reduce the need for more formal treatment in some families.

OB/GYN appointments are a recommended time to screen for Postpartum Mood Disorders and help educate women about maternal depression. Women are more likely to follow through with treatment when they have a trusting relationship with their provider, whom they feel can understand their daily and cultural realities. Furthermore, traditional therapies used to treat Depression in low-income women and women of color may need to be adapted to address situational stressors. More emphasis should be placed on engaging women in treatment, alternative options such as phone interventions should be offered in addition to face-to-face options, and support groups should be made accessible in multiple languages and locations.

If you are a mother living in poverty, know that there are resources for you and there are providers who will honor and respect your unique struggles. If you are a provider reading this booklet, know that you have a unique opportunity to learn about and address the socioeconomic and cultural factors that affect a woman's experience with Postpartum Mood Disorders. Every mother deserves accessible, affordable, culturally relevant, and linguistically appropriate treatment options for Postpartum Mood Disorders. The benefits to these women, their families, and the community as a whole will be invaluable.

Depression in Adoptive Mothers

Although the primary focus of this booklet is on Mood Disorders follow-ing childbirth, our discussion would not be complete without mentioning Mood Disorders following adoption. There are many very understandable reasons why we so frequently see Depression in this situation. Many newly adoptive parents have spent years trying to conceive a child. Their unfulfilled hopes may cause unrealistic expectations about what it will be like to be a parent, and they are often left unprepared for the grief and sadness they may feel when finally having a child to call their own.

As with all new parents, they may feel guilty about their feelings of ambivalence, disappointment, and resentment toward their new child. The belief that there will be an instant bond with their baby is often an unrealistic one. Falling in love with a child is a process, with initial excitement and euphoria giving way to the frequently challenging process of adjusting to the daily presence and demands of another person.

New adoptive mothers who become depressed often silently suffer without asking for help from those around them. Many mothers worry that if they discuss their feelings with their adoption agency or social worker, those same people will view them as unfit parents and remove the new child from their care. These concerns are similar to those of mothers who have just given birth. As a result of these fears, the Depression worsens due to lack of support and understanding. In many cases, often having witnessed years of struggles with infertility, extended family members don't understand why the new mother isn't ecstatically happy that she finally has exactly what she has wanted. Rather than confuse and disappoint her family, many new adoptive mothers remain quietly miserable, filled with shame, guilt, and feelings of worthlessness, believing that somehow, in some way, something is wrong with them, and they have no outlet to speak about it.

Postpartum Mood Disorders Affect the Whole Family

Needless to say, a Postpartum Mood Disorder affects the entire family. For the partners, the changes in their spouse can be frightening and traumatizing. This affects their own ability to function and carry on daily responsibilities.

> **Jaimen, a first time mother, had her mother stay with her and her husband, Tom, for two weeks following the birth of her baby. Although Jaimen and her mother had conflicts throughout their lives, the time seemed to go well. After her mother left, however, Jaimen began experiencing anxious feelings every time the baby cried. She felt outraged at Tom's**

ability to leave and go to work, and she started having Panic Attacks at the thought of being alone with the baby. She pleaded for Tom to stay home. He stayed home for two days and then began fearing he would lose his job. His initial response was supportive, but he soon became angry, confused, and frustrated at his wife's inability to cope with their new baby. Their disagreements escalated into constant fights. He began to stay at work longer to avoid the fighting. Tom's response was to stay away from the tension at home because he did not understand it, and he felt resentful and helpless to change the situation.

The range of responses that occurs between spouses and partners depends somewhat on the general stability and communication level of the couple before the baby arrives. The partner may initially provide support, but if the symptoms continue, this support can turn into denial, followed by fear. Anxiety can then lead to anger and despair. If this is their first child, they may feel "this must be what it's like to have a baby, and it will never get better." Many men feel helpless and afraid as their wives become increasingly dependent on them. Some might also feel guilty and believe they have failed to "make everything okay." Because men are not as inclined to talk about their problems, and there is strong pressure to be happy after a baby is born, the husband may also feel isolated and alone.

Jaimen not only felt overwhelmed by the demands of a new infant, she also felt guilty and ashamed of her own fear. She felt especially fearful of Tom's frustration with her. Her response was to be self-critical and condemning, by telling herself what a bad mother and wife she was. Mothers like Jaimen tend to blame themselves for their Postpartum Mood Disorder, and then feel immense shame and guilt. These feelings in turn can negatively affect all family members.

Sometimes a Postpartum Mood Disorder influences a mother's attachment relationship with her baby. The mother may feel little connection with the baby, which can reinforce her feelings of failure, and result in loss of self-esteem and lack of trust in herself. Or, she may be so anxiously enmeshed with the baby that she disregards everyone else in the family, especially her partner and other children. Both of these scenarios can cause stress on the entire family. If the Postpartum Mood Disorder goes untreated, it can undermine infant development, as well as the long-term health of the marriage and family. With treatment, most negative effects will gradually resolve. In situations like this, all family members need to understand Postpartum Mood Disorders and be involved in the treatment plan.

The Impact of Untreated Postpartum Mood Disorders on Children

At every stage of development, babies are attuned to their mother's mood, her stress level, and her level of attachment. Untreated Depression or Anxiety in a pregnant mother can hinder prenatal bonding, which can lead to long-term consequences for both the mother and baby. If an untreated Mood Disorder persists into the postpartum period, there is an increased likelihood of impaired mother-infant interactions. In addition, recent studies point to health risks for the baby and the mother if the mother has a Mood Disorder during pregnancy.

Simply stated, stress of any kind can negatively affect your pregnancy and perhaps influence your baby's development. Theoretically, this is because cortisol, one of the body's stress hormones, can affect blood flow to the uterus and placenta, and may decrease the flow of nutrients and oxygen to the baby. Untreated Depression and Anxiety during pregnancy are associated with increased rates of miscarriage, preterm delivery, pregnancy induced hypertension, and low birth weight babies. At birth, some of these babies may be labeled "small for gestational age," have lower Apgar scores, and breastfeed less. In addition, babies prenatally exposed to Depression and Anxiety also demonstrate more withdrawal, irritability, and inconsolability. Thus, if you are depressed during pregnancy, every effort should be made to treat your Mood Disorder, to lower stress, and to restore balance to your life.

Studies also show that when a mother is depressed, it changes the environment in which the child is raised. Mothers with a Postpartum

Mood Disorder usually have less capacity to function in some or all of the various roles in their lives. They may have a difficult time following through with medical recommendations such as health prevention, both for themselves and their babies. In addition, women with symptoms of Depression or Anxiety tend to breastfeed for a shorter duration. Babies with poor weight gain are twice as likely to have a mother with symptoms of Depression.

Depression is a disorder marked by withdrawal, and when superimposed on a critical period of bonding and attachment, it can cause long-term problems in the mother-child relationship. Mothers who are depressed show decreased ability to read the cues provided by their babies, and are less responsive to the cues offered by their babies. They tend to be less attentive to issues of safety and to not be as involved with stimulation of the child. Babies of depressed mothers therefore often show less ability to self-regulate and have less ability to self-soothe. This may lead to a vicious cycle, as the mother begins to perceive her baby as having a difficult temperament, which makes it harder for her to engage, which in turn impacts the baby's behavior. Mothers with Depression also report higher rates of infant sleep difficulties, compounding an already difficult situation.

It is important to note that this information is not provided to add to any feelings of guilt or shame that you or any mother with postpartum mood symptoms is likely experiencing, but to place urgency on the need for treatment. The overriding concern is that untreated Mood Disorders may become a chronic problem. In these instances, there is very real concern that children and families will be negatively affected. Thus, this information is provided to underscore the need for early identification, recognition, and treatment of Mood Disorders in the perinatal and postpartum periods. Early identification leads to early treatment, and early treatment leads to healthier mothers, babies, and families.

What to do if you Suspect you May Have a Postpartum Mood Disorder

Prevention is essential to maternal wellness

Most often prenatal preparation focuses on the development of the baby as well as the birth itself. It should, however, also include imparting an understanding of the physical and emotional changes that will occur in the mother during both the prenatal and postpartum phases of pregnancy and birth. Exploring family and personal history, expectations of parenthood, and general coping skills for stress management may all be areas to look at in assessing a healthy adjustment to parenting. The prenatal period is a wonderful time to seek out counseling to work through any unresolved feelings, emotions, or concerns that may be causing you stress or that might impact your journey into parenthood.

Expectant parents can and should ask themselves, their healthcare providers, and childbirth educators, "what will parenthood change about me as a person and what is likely to happen to us as a couple?" Although no health care provider can say for sure how becoming a parent will affect you personally, they can give you a good sense of the normal emotional responses that often follow, and how to recognize the warning signs of adjustment difficulties.

Questions a prenatal care provider should ask:

- Have you ever been diagnosed with Depression, Anxiety, Bipolar Disorder, Psychosis, or an Eating Disorder?
- Have you ever been diagnosed with Depression, Anxiety, Bipolar Disorder, Psychosis, or an Eating Disorder during pregnancy or the postpartum period?
- Have you ever taken any psychotropic medications?
- Have you ever abused alcohol or drugs?
- Have you ever had severe PMS or PMDD (Premenstrual Syndrome or Premenstrual Dysphoric Disorder)?
- Do you have a family history of mental illness or substance abuse?
- Do you have a personal or family history of Thyroid Disorder?

- Since pregnant, how have you been feeling physically and emotionally?
- Do you feel as if you have high levels of stress in your life?
- Does your relationship with your partner make you feel safe?
- Are you satisfied with the level of support you are receiving from your partner, friends, and family?
- Are you experiencing any particular life stressors (such as moving, a job change, financial problems, or a death in the family)?
- How do you feel about your pregnancy?
- Is this a wanted/planned pregnancy?
- Have there been any health problems for you or the baby?
- Did you experience any sexual, physical, or emotional abuse during childhood?
- Have you experienced a trauma, such as a sexual assault, or do you have a history of sexual abuse?
- Are you finding your monthly income sufficient to meet your family's needs?

Total prevention of Postpartum Mood Disorders cannot be assured, but the following can make a difference:

- Know your risk factors for Postpartum Mood Disorders. Educate yourself about the signs, symptoms, and know your own personal triggers and limitations.
- Recognize the importance of the changes a baby will bring to your life.
- Evaluate your personal expectations of being a new parent. Are they realistic?
- Keep the lines of communication with your husband or partner open. Discuss your expectations of becoming parents together, and address difficulties as they arise. Understanding the different expectations that each partner brings to this new situation can help to clarify roles, decrease misunderstandings, and set the stage for open communication when challenges arise in the future.
- Establish and know how to find support and good self-care before the baby arrives.

- Know that therapeutic interventions are available for someone who has had a history of Depression or Anxiety that can help prevent or lessen the intensity of a Postpartum Mood Disorder. Develop a comprehensive intervention plan for yourself now, in the event that any symptoms may arise.

- When issues do arise during pregnancy or the postpartum period, talk them over with a health care provider, therapist, or family member who is familiar with pregnancy/postpartum issues and can help provide a realistic response to your concerns. You are your own best advocate. If you feel you are not being heard or your concerns are being minimized, search for another provider. The earlier the interventions take place the more likely that early recovery will follow.

Assessment

There are two validated tools for screening for Postpartum Mood Disorders. The first one was validated in 1987 and is a 10 item scale called the Edinburgh Postnatal Depression Scale (EPDS). This scale offers a quick assessment of general depressive symptoms seen in Postpartum Mood Disorders. It is especially useful for assessing severity and tracking improvements.

A recent study in 2008 indicated that the EPDS may be further reduced to a three question version which can be used to screen for Postpartum Depression. Due to the prevalence of anxiety symptoms among women with Postpartum Depression, the authors chose a screening tool using the 3 items which comprise the anxiety subscale of the EPDS:

1. I have blamed myself unnecessarily when things went wrong.
2. I have been anxious or worried for no good reason.
3. I have felt scared or panicky for no good reason.

This study indicated that the short version of the EPDS had greater sensitivity and thus may be a better screening tool than the full version of the EPDS.

The second validated screening tool was introduced in 2002 and is called the Postpartum Depression Screening Scale (PDSS). It offers a more thorough assessment of specific symptoms of different Postpartum Mood Disorders including anxiety, guilt, emotional lability, loss of self, mental confusion, and suicidal thoughts. It is a 35 item scale that is particularly useful in the evaluative phase. Both tools are available for clinical use. Please see references for information needed to access to these tools.

Treatment for Postpartum Mood Disorders

Treatment for Postpartum Mood Disorders is optimal when it employs a holistic approach and when it includes medical as well as non-medical interventions. Moms who use this approach tend to get better faster and have a more complete recovery with fewer relapses. If you have mood symptoms at any time in the first year and a half postpartum, you should call your health care provider. Ask questions, list your symptoms and their duration, and voice your concerns. *If your health care provider minimizes your concerns or is not helpful, seek out other resources, such as therapists, psychiatrists, or psychiatric nurse practitioners with knowledge and expertise in treating Postpartum Mood Disorders.* Get involved in postpartum support groups with other new mothers. Above all, speak up about what you are experiencing. Do not suffer alone in silence.

Non-Medical Interventions

Information, education and validation

Learning about Postpartum Mood Disorders, understanding the different causal factors, and validating that what you have is real often helps tremendously. Reading about other women's stories, hearing that many new parents have had the same symptoms you now feel, and knowing that you are not alone offers great hope for recovery. It is important that both the person experiencing the symptoms, as well as their family members, understand that no one is at fault for the Postpartum Mood Disorder. This also means you cannot wish it away. Acceptance of what is happening, and a willingness to work with the symptoms and problems you face is an important step on the road to healing. Denying that anything is wrong, or thinking that it will just go away on its own, only delays the time until treatment can begin, and prolongs the time that you and you family are not functioning optimally together.

Self-care

Self-care can play an integral role in healing from a Postpartum Mood Disorder. Self-care should involve getting adequate sleep, eating well, getting adequate exercise, and stress reduction activities. New mothers are often acutely sleep deprived. Disruptions to the normal sleep cycle (due to infant care) can contribute to or exacerbate depressive or anxious symptoms. Sleep also helps the body repair itself, helps maintain an adequate supply of breast milk, and plays a key role in regulating stress hormones. Therefore, it is important for mothers to rest or nap when their baby naps and to set realistic expectations for what they can accomplish in a day. Morning exercise and regularly scheduled meals can help maintain the normal capacity for sleep, too. In general, sleep must occur in blocks of at least three hours if it is to be physiologically restorative. This may mean that fathers and family members will need to help care for the baby so the mother can get adequate blocks of sleep.

Exercise is also essential to good mental health. Research has shown a strong link between exercise and mood, likely because exercise increases the body's production of endorphins, our "feel good" hormones. Many new mothers may find it difficult to start or return to an exercise routine after giving birth. It takes time for your body to heal sufficiently so that you can exercise at pre-pregnancy levels, and if you are depressed and exhausted, you might not want to exercise at all. Start with small steps. Even a short 10 or 20 minute walk 3 times a week can help improve your mood, and as this happens, you can increase the amount and intensity of exercise.

Other stress reduction techniques might also be helpful, including massage, which has been shown to help relieve pain and stress, and can trigger the release of endorphins and serotonin, both of which help to regulate mood. Yoga, an ancient system of relaxation, exercise and healing, with roots in Indian philosophy, can also be of great benefit on physical, emotional, and spiritual levels. An additional benefit of yoga is the strong focus on awareness of breath, which can help modify and regulate feelings of anxiety. Practicing deep breathing exercises can help you to relax in a matter of minutes, and can be used unobtrusively in a variety of places.

Meditation is another relaxation technique that can also assist in recovery from a Postpartum Mood Disorder. Other simple practices include self-guided imagery, whereby closing your eyes, focusing on your breath, and visualizing a place or sensation of calm, helps you to relax and reduce feelings of stress.

Self-care is a necessary part of recovery, and includes regular breaks from the many demands of motherhood. Invite your mother, sister, or girlfriend to come over and sit with the baby so you can get out for a walk, take a trip to the market alone (yes, even this can feel like a break), or even a short trip to the mall. Even better, have someone care for the baby while you nap, take a long bath, or go get a massage. Above all, take time to create balance between the demands of caring for a newborn and the needs for restoration through self-care.

Taking care of yourself also includes eating healthy foods. Inadequate intake of calories, or an imbalance of carbohydrates, protein, or fats can lead to generalized nutritional deficiencies that can ultimately affect many areas of health, including emotional well-being. If you have concerns in this area, seek consultation from a qualified provider such as a nutritionist or naturopathic physician.

Omega-3 fatty acids are a particularly important component of a healthy diet for women with a Postpartum Mood Disorder. Omega-3 fatty acids, which are found in oils such as flaxseed, black current, walnuts, and fish oils (especially EPA and DHA) play a critical role in the development and functioning of the nervous system, and may also help promote hormone and immune system functioning. Individuals with Depression have been shown to have lower DHA levels than those without Depression. Low levels of other Omega-3 fatty acids have also been correlated with increased severity of Depression. Some individuals with Depression have tried taking large doses of supplemental Omega-3 fatty acids, or enough fish oil to contain 9.6 grams of Omega-3 fatty acids per day, for at least four months, and have noted alleviation or lessening of their symptom. Though Omega-3 fatty acids have never been shown to "cure" Depression, supplementation with them has well established health benefits, and thus Omega-3 fatty acids can play an important role in enhancing a mother's overall wellness. Other nutritional supplements may be helpful in some cases of Depression. Anemia due to iron deficiency is known to affect mood and can worsen symptoms of Depression. This must be diagnosed and treated by a medical/naturopathic physician, a nurse midwife, or a nurse practitioner. The treatment in some cases may be as simple as iron supplementation.

Individuals suffering from chronic Depression should also be evaluated for possible folic acid and/or B-Vitamin deficiency (especially Vitamins B1, B6, and B12). Vitamin B6 is necessary for the formation of serotonin, but it is depleted during pregnancy unless adequate amounts are taken as a dietary supplement. One research project found that Vitamin B6, when given for one month postpartum, significantly reduced the expected rate of occurrence of postpartum emotional symptoms among women who had a history of a previous postpartum mood episode. Specific amounts of B6 should be discussed between you and your health care provider. Breastfeeding mothers should always consult a physician or nurse practitioner with adequate knowledge of nutrition to assure the correct dosing of B-vitamins, as high doses of Vitamin B6 can inhibit breast milk production.

Social support

Family support and/or support from close friends is absolutely vital for early recovery from a Postpartum Mood Disorder. Support means help with physical care for the parent, baby, and household, for as long as the parent needs to rebuild her physical energy. That may also include having a family member, friend, or hired doula available 24 hours a day during the most intense times.

Doulas are women who are specially trained to provide support to mothers during labor and/or the postpartum period. The role of the doula is not new but has been revived in recent years, perhaps due to the lack of support available to mothers from their extended families in these transient times in many Western cultures. The word doula comes from the Greek word for "woman's servant." The assistance of a doula has been proven through research to improve both the physical and psychological well-being of the mother. Studies show among doula-supported mothers, an increased satisfaction with motherhood, better attunement with their newborns, and more success in breastfeeding. Studies also show that this kind of support is beneficial to new fathers as well.

Emotional support means understanding the person's fears and pain, primarily through empathic listening and validation. Listening and hearing a woman's concerns, and never minimizing them, is essential to making her feel cared for. This also means recognizing the limits of what a family member can and cannot do. Seeking skilled professional help for the new mother, and in some cases, for all family members, might very well become necessary to help sort out all the issues.

Extended family and community can provide important help during the most difficult times. The extended family members may need to be brought in for lengthy stretches of time during the acute phase of the Mood Disorder. It is important to recognize that the Mood Disorder may take months to fully recover from.

Postpartum support groups, particularly those focusing on Postpartum Mood Disorders, can be helpful for information, validation of symptoms, and as a place to share your fears, overwhelming feelings, and hopes for recovery.

Fathers and partners

Fathers and partners need support themselves during the postpartum period, and more so when their partner has a Postpartum Mood Disorder. Until recently, not much has been available for them. Now there are web sites for fathers, books focusing on fatherhood and the importance of fathers in child development, support groups for new fathers, and other resources recognizing the importance of the father's role in parenting a new baby. There are also the beginnings of support networks starting to form for gay and lesbian couples. In some communities, support groups are available through private therapy practices, mental health clinics, and local hospitals.

Counseling

As mentioned, part of offering good support to a new mother experiencing postpartum mood symptoms means recognizing the limits of what family members and friends can and cannot do. Seeking the assistance of a licensed professional therapist, psychiatrist, nurse practitioner, or psychologist who is knowledgeable in the treatment of women and families experiencing Postpartum Mood Disorders is a healthy, and often essential, step to take in order to promote recovery.

A therapist can help a new mother realize that what she is experiencing has a name. They can also help educate her about her symptoms, the typical course of the different Postpartum Mood Disorders, and can work with her to help her set goals to optimize wellness.

It is crucial to remember that no one brings on a Postpartum Mood Disorder intentionally. There is no one to blame for its occurrence. But, by the same token, one cannot just wish it away. When it happens, recognizing and working with the feelings of fear, anger, shame and hurt is much more effective than trying to ignore them. Emotional stress reduction includes recognizing distorted thought patterns, such as self-blame. Consciously reducing negative thoughts and learning ways to take small positive steps in the direction of wellness will begin to decrease emotional stress and reactivity.

Therapy teaches ways to recognize and change disturbing thoughts, manage feelings of anxiety and panic, increase positive coping skills, and build self-esteem. Cognitive Behavioral Therapy (CBT) is one therapeutic modality that has been shown to be very effective in treating Postpartum Mood Disorders. It is based on the understanding that the way we think and act affects the way we feel. Depressed women often have many negative thoughts. In Cognitive Behavioral Therapy, the therapist helps the woman set manageable goals, identify her distorted thinking patterns, and replace these thoughts with more realistic ones.

Many new parents hope and imagine how they will parent differently from their own parents. Becoming aware of, and working to resolve, any old family patterns you disliked as a child will help you parent the way you choose to, rather than simply repeating parenting styles that mimic the ways in which you were raised. Therapy can help with this process and can build insight into your own motivations and aspirations as a parent.

As mentioned, it is important to seek a psychotherapist who specializes in treatment within the context of having a baby, and recognizes the adjustment to motherhood as an integral part of treatment. *The combination of support, psychotherapy, and medication (if necessary), is the most effective treatment approach.*

For specific providers who are knowledgeable in working with Postpartum Mood Disorders, please call the PSI of WA Warm Line for referrals, at 888.404.PPMD, or visit www.ppmdsupport.com.

Treatment:
Three Critical Components

Medical Intervention

Therapeutic Intervention

Social Support

Medical Intervention

Pregnancy, delivery, breastfeeding, sleep deprivation, and the 24 hour demands of caring for a newborn can place tremendous stress on a woman's nervous and hormonal systems. During pregnancy, levels of estrogen, progesterone, and cortisol rise to very high levels and then decline dramatically at birth. Some women are especially sensitive to these changes for reasons that are not entirely clear, rendering them more vulnerable to mood changes during pregnancy and in the postpartum period.

When a woman develops a Mood Disorder during the postpartum period, she should tell her medical provider so that any underlying medical causes for the Mood Disorder can be investigated. This includes looking for abnormalities in a woman's blood that might explain her mood. For example, some women develop altered thyroid activity and anemia during pregnancy and the postpartum period, both of which can contribute to mood symptoms and unusually low energy. Indeed, Hypothyroidism, or "low thyroid," occurs in 5 to 9 percent of postpartum women and can cause depressive symptoms, lethargy, fatigue, and low motivation. Usually, after starting thyroid hormone replacement, the mother's mood improves and she feels back to her "normal" self. Assessing thyroid function is a normal part of a Depression work-up and can be done by your OB/GYN, nurse-midwife, family doctor, nurse practitioner, or psychiatrist. Clinical or subclinical Hypothyroidism is determined by checking blood levels of thyroid stimulating hormone, and may need to be checked more than once during the first postpartum year.

Anemia can also present with symptoms similar to Anxiety or Depression. During pregnancy, most women are tested for anemia, but few are routinely tested at their six-week postpartum check up. A complete postpartum psychiatric evaluation should also include testing for anemia, and if a mother is anemic, she should receive iron replacement therapy. If you have any concerns about your physical symptoms, and think you may have some underlying health problems that are contributing to your mood, let your healthcare provider know your concerns. In some instances, a simple blood test may provide answers.

Medications for Postpartum Mood Disorders

Medical decision making

Deciding whether or not to take medications to treat Postpartum Depression or Anxiety is highly personal. Physicians or nurse practitioners who specialize in the care of women with Postpartum Mood Disorders are usually very sensitive to a woman's personal preferences, her cultural and religious beliefs, as well as any strongly held beliefs about taking psychiatric medication. Although much progress has been made, many women still feel ashamed and stigmatized by Depression and other Mood Disorders. Many women judge themselves harshly when depressed, as though they were somehow at fault for their Depression or Anxiety, or, as though their Depression means something about their ability to be a good mother. Statements such as "this means I wasn't cut out to be a mother" or "everybody else is a better mother than I am" are frequently heard from these mothers. With severe Postpartum Depression, some mothers believe that "the baby would be better off without me." Professionals who specialize in the treatment of Postpartum Mood Disorders can reassure the mother that she is not to blame, that her Depression does not mean she is or will be a bad mother, and that with proper treatment, these thoughts will go away. Sometimes a mother believes that if she were strong enough, she would not need medication. A good psychiatric health care provider should help dispel this myth. Depression or Anxiety Disorders cannot be willed away by simply "toughing it out" or by "being stronger." Acquiring a Postpartum Mood Disorder is not a woman's fault, and accepting medications to treat the disorder is not in any way an admission of weakness or failure.

When deciding to treat a Postpartum Mood Disorder with medications, the mother should discuss with her provider the risks and benefits of treatment versus the risks and benefits of not receiving treatment. One risk of medication includes exposing the baby to medication via the breast milk. If the baby is bottle-feeding, this is not an issue. Since the 1990s, many breastfeeding mothers have been treated with common types of antidepressant medications, from a category known as the Selective Serotonin Reuptake Inhibitors (SSRIs), and many studies have examined the effects of these medications on babies. SSRIs that have been used and studied in this way include Zoloft, Prozac, Celexa, and Paxil. Although research has confirmed that breastfeeding mothers on an antidepressant medication do transfer some of the medication to their baby, it is important to understand that the amount of medication in the baby's blood is usually not detectable, or is detectable at a very low level. Dr. Zachary Stowe, of Emory University in Atlanta, has put exposure to the baby in perspective by noting the baby's annual dose of Zoloft or Prozac is at most two times the mother's dose on a single day. Furthermore, studies have failed to show any adverse effects in the infant from this amount of exposure. Thus far, long-term studies looking at children well into school age show no differences between the children who were exposed to medication through breastfeeding and a control population who were not.

Sometimes mothers think that not taking medications is safest, and therefore, best for their baby. Mothers should know, however, there are risks associated with receiving no treatment or in postponing treatment as well. Often a Mood Disorder becomes harder to treat the longer it goes untreated, and having severe, long-term Depression poses significant risk for developing future episodes of Depression. Indeed, several researchers describe a kindling phenomenon whereby repeated episodes of untreated Depression lead to repeated illness, a progressively greater severity of illness with each episode, and increasingly poorer responses to treatment.

In addition, the longer the mother remains depressed or highly anxious, the longer her family is affected by her illness. As previously mentioned, untreated Postpartum Depression is a risk factor for problems in the infant's development, and thus treating the mother would potentially avert these problems, and accordingly be of benefit to both mother and baby. Infants whose mothers are depressed have greater risk for developing Mood Disorders themselves, especially when they become adolescents. Infant boys seem to be most vulnerable to this effect. Also, untreated Depression in mothers is a major predictor of negative parenting behaviors (such as yelling or spanking), and each additional symptom of Depression decreases the likelihood that the mother will exhibit positive parenting behaviors (such as making eye contact or playing with the child). Therefore, most providers try to treat the mother early and to resolve the symptoms not only to help the mother, but also to lessen the impact of Depression on the developing infant.

It is necessary that you and your family have access to information with which you can make an informed choice while weighing the risks and the benefits of each treatment option. If you have unanswered questions or concerns, please seek consultation from a qualified provider.

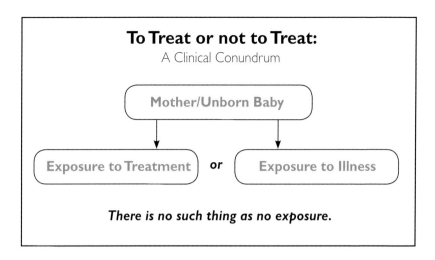

To Treat or not to Treat:
A Clinical Conundrum

Mother/Unborn Baby

Exposure to Treatment *or* Exposure to Illness

There is no such thing as no exposure.

Antidepressant medications

Serotonin is a brain chemical (neurotransmitter) that helps promote normal mood and sleep. The decreased estrogen during the immediate postpartum period influences the availability of serotonin in the brain. This decreased availability is thought to play a pivotal role in the development of Depression, Anxiety, and sleep problems often seen in postpartum women. There are many studies demonstrating the effectiveness of antidepressants in treating Postpartum Mood Disorders.

Antidepressant medications are non-addictive substances that help restore normal brain chemistry by increasing serotonin and other brain chemicals, which can thereby reduce the symptoms of Postpartum Depression and Anxiety. Antidepressants typically begin to work in 4 to 6 weeks for about 85 percent of patients whose symptoms arise during or following pregnancy. A psychiatrist, physician or nurse practitioner with experience in treating postpartum and breastfeeding women should prescribe these medications and should monitor the mother closely. Because many mothers are concerned about taking medications while breastfeeding, medical providers typically choose an antidepressant that has minimal secretion into the breast milk. In many cases, the mother's depressed mood has been shown to have greater long-term negative effects on the child than the impact of very small amounts of antidepressant medication transmitted to the child through the mother's breast milk. This important and very personal discussion should occur between the mother and her psychiatric provider.

Many antidepressants are considered safe for use during breastfeeding, although no medication has formal FDA approval for use in breastfeeding. The medications considered the safest are Zoloft and Paxil. These medications are called Selective Serotonin Reuptake Inhibitors (SSRIs). Other SSRIs are also considered relatively safe during breastfeeding, but some mild adverse effects have been reported in infants exposed to these medicines at high doses. Please discuss this with a knowledgeable medical provider familiar with the use of psychotropic medications in the postpartum period. Another category of antidepressants called tricyclic antidepressants (TCAs) are also considered safe. Nortriptyline and Desipramine are two examples of these, but they are not commonly used because the SSRIs are equally effective, and have fewer side effects for the mother. Antidepressants also play an important role in treating the symptoms of Postpartum Anxiety Disorders.

Sometimes mothers are initially quite sensitive to the SSRIs, so it is common to start at a low dose and then slowly increase the dose to allow the body to get used to the medicine. These medicines take time to work and a mother should not expect her symptoms to resolve immediately.

Typically, mothers experience improvement in their symptoms within 4 to 6 weeks of starting treatment. Some individuals might also need an anti-anxiety medication temporarily while waiting for the antidepressant to work (see below, anti-anxiety medications). The length of time you are on these medications is highly individual, and should be discussed with your provider.

Mood stabilizers

Mood stabilizers are a group of medications used to treat Bipolar Disorder, which act to "stabilize" mood by preventing the highs and lows of this disorder. Examples include Lithium, Depakote, Lamotrigine (Lamictal), and Carbamezapine (Tegretol). Some mood stabilizing medications used to treat Bipolar Disorder may be safe for use during pregnancy, but not during breastfeeding. In general, Lithium is used, when necessary, during the second and third trimester of pregnancy, but is not safe for use while breastfeeding. Depakote and Tegretol are safe for use during breastfeeding but not during pregnancy. As you can see, the medication management of women with Bipolar Disorder is quite complicated. Therefore, if you have Bipolar Disorder, you should work closely with a specialist during pregnancy and the postpartum period.

Some women whose Bipolar Disorder has not yet manifested may have their first mood episode following the birth; this typically occurs in the early postpartum period. In this situation, Mania is the most common mood experienced, but severe depressive symptoms can occur as well. As previously stated, Mania is characterized by such things as elated or very irritable moods, high levels of activity, feelings of grandiosity, decreased need for sleep, impulsiveness, racing thoughts, and pressured, rapid, or loud speech. It is often accompanied by poor judgment that leads to impulsive activities such as increased spending, drug or alcohol use, and heightened sexuality, as well as thoughts that are loosely connected, making it hard to focus.

It may be difficult for the untrained professional to recognize Hypomania, Mania, or Depression as occurring in the setting of a bipolar illness, so it is extremely important for mothers to be referred to a specialist for diagnosis and treatment, especially if Bipolar Disorder runs in the family. This is because when Mania or Hypomania goes untreated or when Bipolar Disorder is treated with SSRIs only, the patient can, in rare instances, become psychotic—a potentially life threatening situation for both mother and/or her baby. Hospitalization is usually needed for the safety of both the mother and baby. Most episodes of Bipolar Disorder, however, do not lead to Psychosis, and can be treated with mood stabilizers. The other reason it is so important for a mother with depressive symptoms to get an accurate diagnosis is that SSRIs typically do not work as well, if at all, for those who actually have a Bipolar Disorder, and can cause problems such as Hypomania, rapid cycling, agitation, and suicidal thoughts. Above all, they delay the time until remission of symptoms, and thus further expose the mother and baby to all the problems and suffering associated with Depression.

Knowledgeable providers are available to help pregnant or breastfeeding women with Bipolar Disorder. Please call the PSI of WA Warm Line, at 888.404.PPMD, for information on where to find these providers.

Antipsychotic medications

Antipsychotics are a class of medications used to treat psychotic illnesses, Bipolar Disorder, and sometimes, to treat severe Depression or treatment-resistant OCD. High potency antipsychotic medications such as Haldol are used in breastfeeding mothers when necessary. Newer antipsychotics such as Zyprexa, Seroquel, Abilify, and Geodon have also been used in pregnant and breastfeeding mothers, and their use should be carefully weighed against the risk of unmedicated or untreated psychiatric illness. Patients who require these medications should receive their care from a qualified and skilled psychiatric provider. Please call the PSI of WA Warm Line, at 888.404.PPMD, for information on where to find these providers.

Anti-anxiety medications

Benzodiazepines are medications that quickly relieve symptoms of Anxiety and are indicated for temporary use of moderate to severe Anxiety. Low doses of certain benzodiazepines can be used effectively and safely in breastfeeding mothers who experience Anxiety and/or Panic Attacks. These should be used temporarily and primarily while the antidepressant is taking effect. Again, a knowledgeable psychiatric provider can help mothers who have an Anxiety Disorder to learn about the use of these medicines during pregnancy and lactation.

Medications for sleep

Sometimes a mother will have severe insomnia that does not respond immediately to the antidepressant medicine. There are certain sleep medications that are compatible with breastfeeding, for example Ambien, Trazadone, and low dose Clonazepam. As with the other medications, an experienced postpartum psychiatric professional should be consulted regarding which types and dosages are considered safe for short-term use.

Alternative Health Practitioners

Some women prefer to see an alternative health practitioner. Examples of those who could be consulted regarding postpartum concerns include midwives, naturopathic physicians, acupuncturists, homeopaths, and craniosacral therapists. The following is meant to provide a brief look at alternative healing modalities, and to bring to awareness the fact that many methods of healing exist. However, the following information should not be seen as a substitute for advice from your medical doctor. If a woman has serious symptoms of Depression and/or Anxiety, or is having thoughts of self-harm, she should first seek the care and guidance of a medical professional in conjunction with a skilled therapist. Alternative modalities may be used as supplementary paths to healing.

Midwifery

For centuries, midwives have been assisting women through the prenatal period, with birth, and with postpartum care. Traditionally female healers, midwives have been recognized in many cultures since ancient times, under various names that are all derived from the same meaning—"with woman." Midwives are usually sensitive to an expectant mother's physical and emotional state, and can offer considerable emotional support for new parents, providing referrals for additional care as needed.

Naturopathic medicine

Naturopathic medicine is a distinct, integrated system of primary health care offered by licensed physicians. A naturopathic doctor is trained in the art and science of natural healing traditions. The body's innate ability to self-heal is accessed with specific focus on lifestyle, disease prevention, and the use of natural modalities to heal disease. These modalities may include herbal medicine, diet modification and supplementation, massage, hydrotherapy, lifestyle counseling, and a wide variety of other healing approaches.

A naturopathic physician may recommend herbal treatments for Depression. Some of these might include St. John's Wort, Siberian ginseng, and Schizandra berry extracts. As with all treatment recommendations, you should weigh the known risks of these treatments against the known benefits of such treatments. You should also compare their efficacy with the efficacy of other treatments and make the decision that feels best to you. Ask your naturopathic provider to help you weigh these risks and benefits, as many herbal remedies used for Depression have side effects and enter the breast milk much in the same way prescription medication does. Also, many herbal remedies have not been studied for use in women with Postpartum Mood Disorders. If you are being treated with an antidepressant and/or with herbs, you need to let both your naturopath and your medical provider know exactly what you are taking as there could be serious interactions between the two that can cause problems. For example, St. John's Wort can interact with some antidepressants, and theoretically cause a complication known as Serotonin Syndrome.

Individuals with Depression or Anxiety who do not respond to other conventional or natural approaches to treatment should consult a naturopathic physician to diagnose possible food sensitivities or allergies. Food allergies can create inflammation in the body that research has demonstrated can contribute to their documented mood-altering effects. Several double-blind studies have shown that food allergies can trigger emotional disorders such as Depression and Anxiety.

Acupuncture

Acupuncture is one of the oldest, most common medical modalities in the world, originating in China thousands of years ago. The fundamental concept in acupuncture involves balancing the flow of our vital energy, called Qi (pronounced "chee"), which creates and fuels our body, mind, and spirit. One of the benefits of acupuncture is that there is no contraindication to treatment, and it does not adversely interact with other treatments, such as conventional antidepressant therapy. It has the added benefit of not interfering with lactation. Research has shown acupuncture to be safe, and it may be a helpful complimentary treatment for many mental health conditions, including Depression.

Homeopathy

Homeopathy is based on the natural law of "like cures like," the idea that a substance that has the ability to produce symptoms in a healthy person will heal an unhealthy person with similar symptoms. Homeopathy tries to address each individual's unique symptoms and usually without concern for unwanted side effects. Homeopathic remedies are considered safe during pregnancy and breastfeeding and will not likely interfere with any other prescription medication you may be taking. It is important to note, however, there is no evidence demonstrating Homeopathy's effectiveness in treating severe Postpartum Mood Disorders, so if you choose to solely use this healing modality, please let your medical provider or therapist know. Please also let your provider know if you are taking homeopathic remedies in addition to medication.

Craniosacral therapy

Craniosacral therapy shares many of the theoretical constructs of the manual practices of Osteopathy, which traces its history back to the early 1900s. Craniosacral therapy is a gentle yet powerful hands-on therapy that benefits whole-body health, and can be a valuable adjunct to the treatment of a wide variety of physical and emotional conditions such as chronic fatigue, insomnia, back and neck pain, Depression, Anxiety, stress and tension-related problems, and Posttraumatic Stress Disorder. This form of bodywork is growing in popularity among midwives, doulas, and other childbirth professionals as a modality that is viewed as complementary to holistic maternity care. Craniosacral therapy is considered to be safe during pregnancy, as it calms the nervous system of both mother and child, encouraging emotional bonding that can otherwise be short-circuited due to prenatal and birth stresses and trauma.

Summary

Becoming a mother can be a richly rewarding, life-changing event. For mothers with Postpartum Mood Disorders, the symptoms of their illness can preclude them from reaping these rewards. The earlier we identify and validate that a Postpartum Mood Disorder exists and needs treatment, the less a family will have to endure this time in painful isolation. All new mothers and families need to know they are not alone, that help is available, and that they can overcome their Postpartum Mood Disorder with proper treatment and support from skilled professionals.

Resources

Local resources:

Postpartum Support International of Washington (PSI of WA)
www.ppmdsupport.com
P.O. Box 15535
Seattle, WA 98115
888.404.PPMD (7763); 24 hour Warm Line
Washington State organization offering support, information and education regarding Postpartum Mood Disorders.

Northwest Association for Postpartum Support
www.napsdoulas.com
Postpartum doula information and referral site.

Speak Up When You're Down
www.wcpcan.wa.gov/ppd/aboutus_campaign.htm
Web site for the Washington State Postpartum Depression (PPD) Awareness Campaign, committed to addressing PPD in ways that will inform, inspire, and impact the future health of women, children and their families in Washington.

General resources:

Bringing Baby Home
www.bbhonline.org
The Bringing Baby Home (BBH) project combines scientific research and service product delivery in order to improve the quality of life for babies and children by strengthening their families. The aim is to promote social change by making the BBH workshop available as part of the standard birth preparation program offered to expectant couples in hospitals throughout the nation.

Doulas of North America
www.dona.org
An international association of doulas who are trained to provide the highest quality emotional, physical, and educational support to women and their families during childbirth and the postpartum period.

MedEd
www.mededppd.org
Excellent site developed with the support of the National Institute of Mental Health (NIMH) to provide education about Postpartum Depression.

The MGH Center for Women's Mental Health

www.womensmentalhealth.org

This site provides a range of current information including discussion of new research findings in women's mental health and how such investigations inform day-to-day clinical practice.

The Online PPD Support Group

www.ppdsupportpage.com

Information, support and assistance to those dealing with Postpartum Mood Disorders, their families, friends, physicians, and counselors.

Postpartum Dads

https://home.comcast.net/~ddklinker/mysite2/Welcome_page.htm

Web site intended to help dads and families by providing firsthand information and guidance through the experience of Postpartum Depression.

Postpartum Progress

www.postpartumprogress.typepad.com

Promoting progress in treatment and care for those with Postpartum Mood Disorders, including Postpartum Depression, Postpartum Obsessive-Compulsive Disorder, and Postpartum Psychosis.

Postpartum Support International

www.postpartum.net

Offering support, information and education regarding Postpartum Mood Disorders.

Trauma and Birth Stress

www.tabs.org.nz

Posttraumatic Stress Disorder suffered as a result of a traumatic birth experience has only recently been recognized. This web site offers comprehensive information and education on birth stress and trauma.

Also check with your local hospital, public health department, and community center for infant/parent classes and other new mom support groups.

Please note: *Postpartum Support International of Washington is not responsible for the contents of any of the web sites listed above, and inclusion in this list does not indicate that PSI of WA is endorsing the policies, procedures, or views contained therein.*

Recommended Books

Recommended reading for parents:

Becoming Parents: How to Strengthen Your Marriage as Your Family Grows. Pamela L. Jordan, Scott M. Stanley, and Howard J. Markman (2001)

Beyond the Blues: A Guide to Understanding and Treating Prenatal and Postpartum Depression. Shoshana Bennett and Pec Indman (2006)

The Birth of a Mother: How the Motherhood Experience Changes You Forever. Daniel N. Stern, Nadia Bruschweiler-Stern, and Alison Freeland (1999)

A Deeper Shade of Blue: A Woman's Guide to Recognizing and Treating Depression in Her Childbearing Years. Ruta Nonacs (2006)

Fatherneed: Why Father Care is as Essential as Mother Care for Your Child. Kyle Pruett (2001)

The Hidden Feelings of Motherhood: Coping with Stress, Depression, and Burnout. Kathleen A. Kendall-Tackett (2005)

The Journey to Parenthood: Myths, Reality and What Really Matters. Diana Lynn Barnes and Leigh Balber (2007)

The Mother-to-Mother Postpartum Depression Support Book. Sandra Poulin (2006)

Mothering the New Mother: Women's Feelings and Needs After Childbirth. Sally Placksin (April 2000)

The Post-Adoption Blues: Overcoming the Unforeseen Challenges of Adoption. Karen J. Foli and John R. Thompson (2004)

Postpartum Depression Demystified: An Essential Guide for Understanding and Beating the Most Common Complication After Childbirth. Joyce A. Venis and Suzanne McCloskey (2007)

Postpartum Depression For Dummies. Shoshana S. Bennett (2007)

The Postpartum Husband: Practical Solutions for Living with Postpartum Depression. Karen R. Kleiman (2001)

Pregnancy Blues: What Every Woman Needs to Know about Depression During Pregnancy. Shaila Kulkarni Misri (2006)

Shouldn't I Be Happy: Emotional Problems of Pregnant and Postpartum Women. Shaila Misri (2002)

What Am I Thinking? Having a Baby After Postpartum Depression. Karen Kleiman (2005)

Recommended reading for professionals:

Depression in New Mothers: Causes, Consequences, and Treatment Alternatives. Kathleen A. Kendall-Tackett (2005)

Medications and Mothers' Milk. Thomas W. Hale (2006)

Mood and Anxiety Disorders During Pregnancy and Postpartum. Lee S. Cohen and Ruta Nonacs (Editors) (2005)

Perinatal and Postpartum Mood Disorders: Perspectives and Treatment Guide for the Health Care Practitioner. Susan Dowd Stone and Alexis Menkin (2008)

Postpartum Depression and Child Development. Lynne Murray and Peter J. Cooper (Editors) (2007)

Postpartum Mood and Anxiety Disorders: A Guide. Cheryl Tatano Beck and Jeanne Watson Driscoll (2005)

Therapy and the Postpartum Woman: Notes on Healing Postpartum Depression for Clinicians and the Women Who Seek Their Help. Karen Kleiman (2008)

When Survivors Give Birth: Understanding and Healing the Effects of Early Sexual Abuse on Childbearing Women. Penny Simkin and Phyllis Klaus (2004)

References

American Psychiatric Association. (2000). Diagnostic and statistical manual of mental disorders: DSM-IV-TR. Washington, DC: Author.

Beck, C. T. (2002). Postpartum Depression Screening Scale, Los Angeles: Western Psychological Services. 800.648.8857.

Bettes, B. (1988). Maternal depression and motherese: Temporal and international features. Child Development, 59, 1089-1096.

Brown M., Gibney, M., Husband, P. & Radcliffe, M. (1981). Food allergy in polysymptomatic patients. Practitioner, 225, 1651–1654.

Campbell, S., Cohn, J. & Meyers, T. (1995). Depression in first-time mothers: Mother-infant interaction and depression chronicity. Developmental Psychobiology, 31(3), 349-357.

Cox, J. L., Holden, J. M. & Sagovsky, R. (1987). Detection of postnatal depression: Development of the 10-item Edinburgh postnatal depression scale. British Journal of Psychiatry, 150, 782-786.

Dawson, G., Hessl, D. & Frey, K. (1994). Social influences on early developing biological and behavioral systems related to risk for affective disorder. Development and Psychopathology, 6, 759-779.

Doskoch, P. (2001). Which is more toxic to a fetus— antidepressants or maternal depression? Neuropsychiatry Reviews, Vol. 2, Number 5.

Edwards, R., Peet, M., Shay, J. & Horrobin, D. (1998). Omega-3 polyunsaturated fatty acid levels in the diet and in red blood cell membranes of depressed patients. Journal of Affective Disorders, 48, 149–155.

Field, T. (1992). Infants of depressed mothers. Development and Psychopathology, 4, 49-66.

Goldsmith, D. & Rogoff, B. (1997). Mothers' and toddlers' coordinated joint focus of attention: Variations with maternal dysphoric symptoms. Developmental Psychology, 33(1), 113-119.

Hamilton, J. & Harberger, P., Eds. (1992). Postpartum psychiatric illness: A picture puzzle. Philadelphia: University of Philadelphia Press.

Journal of Midwifery and Women's Health, 49(2): 96-103, 2004. Complementary therapies in treatment of postpartum depression. (Accessed December 11, 2008) http://www.medscape.com/viewarticle/471895_6

Kabir K., Sheeder J. & Kelly L. S. (2008). Identifying postpartum depression: Are 3 questions as good as 10? Pediatrics, 122(3): e696-e702.

Kennedy, H., Beck, C. & Driscoll, J. (2002). A light in the fog: Caring for women with postpartum depression. Journal of Midwifery and Women's Health, 47(5), 318-330.

Kessler, R. C. et al. (1994). Lifetime and 12-month prevalence of DSM-III-R psychiatric disorders in the United States. Results from the National Comorbidity Survey. Archives of General Psychiatry, Jan, 51(1): 8-19.

King, D. (1981). Can allergic exposure provoke psychological symptoms? A double-blind test. Biological Psychiatry, 16, 3–19.

Knitzer, J., Theberge, S. & Johnson, K. (January 2008). Reducing maternal depression and its impact on young children: Toward a responsive early childhood policy framework. Project Three Issue Brief, No. 2, National Center for Children in Poverty; Colombia University. http://www.nccp.org/publications/pub_791.html

Kruckman, L. (1992). Rituals and Support: An Anthropological View of Postpartum Depression in J. Hamilton & P. Harberger, Postpartum psychiatric illness: A picture puzzle, 137-149. Philadelphia: University of Philadelphia Press.

Kumar, C., McIvor, R., Davies, T., Brown, N., Papadopoulos, A., Wieck, A., Checkley, S. A., Campbell, I. C. & Marks, M. N. (2003). Estrogen administration does not reduce the rate of recurrence of affective psychosis after childbirth. Journal of Clinical Psychiatry, 64(2), 112-118.

NAMI Multicultural Action Center (June 2003). American Indian and Alaska Native communities mental health fact sheet. (Accessed December 2008). http://www.womenshealth.gov/minority/americanindian/mh.cfm

NAMI Multicultural Action Center (2004). Asian American mental health fact sheet. (Accessed December 2008). http://www.womenshealth.gov/minority/asianamerican/mh.cfm

Newport, D. J., Hostetter, A. H., Arnold, A. & Stowe, Z. N. (2002). The treatment of postpartum depression: Minimizing infant exposures. Journal of Clinical Psychiatry, 63 (7), 31-44.

O'Connor et al. (2002). Maternal antenatal anxiety and children's be-havioural/emotional problems at 4 years: Report from the Avon Longitudinal Study of Parents and Children. British Journal of Psychiatry, 180, 502-508.

O'Connor et al. (2003). Maternal antenatal anxiety and behavioural/emotional problems in children: A test of a programming hypothesis. Journal of Child Psychology and Psychiatry, 44(7), 1025-1036.

Ramos, D. (2008). Depression in Women. Etiology and Management Strategies. Los Angeles, CA. www.nmqf.org/presentations/08C7RamosDE.pdf

Spencer, K. M. (2008). Craniosacral Therapy in the Midwifery Model of Care. Midwifery Today, 87.

Stoll, A. et al. (1999). Omega 3 fatty acids in bipolar disorder. A preliminary double-blind, placebo-controlled trial. Archives of General Psychiatry, 56, 407–412.

Tronick, E. Z. (1989). Emotions and emotional communication in infants. American Psychologist, 44(2), 112-119.

U.S. Department of Health and Human Services, Health Resources and Services Administration (2005). Women's Health USA 2005. Rockville, Maryland: U.S. Department of Health and Human Services.

Van Den Bergh & Marcoen (2004). Child Development. July/August, 75(4), 1085-1097.

Weissman, A. M. et al. (2004). Pooled analysis of antidepressant levels in lactating mothers, breast milk, and nursing infants. American Journal of Psychiatry, June, 161(6):1066-78.

Wisner, K. & Wheeler, S. B. (1994). Prevention of recurrent postpartum major depression. Hospital & Community Psychiatry, 45(12): 1191-6.

Wisner, K. L., Parry, B. L. & Piontek, C. M. (2002). Postpartum depression. New England Journal of Medicine, 347(3), 194-199.

Biographies

Original text written by:

Dawn Simon Gruen, MSW, ACSW was a pioneer in the field of postpartum support beginning in the 1970s. Her career in Seattle began at Family Services of King County, where she established the Family Life Education Program. Subsequently, Dawn set up a private practice in psychotherapy for many years in Seattle, during which time she helped many women and families. Dawn's focus was working with perinatal adjustments and balancing work and family issues. Dawn passed away in 1999. Her work continues through such avenues as the Depression After Delivery organization (now known as Postpartum Support International of Washington), and the PSI of WA-funded scholarship for postpartum psychotherapy. Dawn was the mother of two children.

Sixth Edition written by:

Juliana K. Nason, MA, LMHC, NCC, CMHS, HBCE is a Licensed Mental Health Counselor, National Certified Counselor, and Child Mental Health Specialist in private practice with an emphasis on perinatal and postpartum counseling for women and their families. She works with issues such as birth trauma, miscarriage and neonatal loss, infertility, Perinatal and Postpartum Mood Disorders, preparing abuse survivors for birth, attachment and bonding, and parenting consultation and support. She has extensive experience providing therapy for children, adults, and families, with additional training in foster care and adoption therapy. Her practice, Chrysalis Counseling Services, is located in downtown Everett. Juliana serves on the Board of Directors for Postpartum Support International of Washington, and was formerly the Washington State Co-Coordinator for Postpartum Support International. She is also a Certified HypnoBirthing Practitioner, providing private childbirth education for growing families. She is the very proud mother of one child.

Patricia Spach, MN, ARNP is a psychiatric mental health nurse practitioner. She received her training at the University of Washington School of Nursing, Department of Psychosocial and Community Health. Her graduate training focused on neurobiological models of stress in adolescent mothers with Postpartum Depression. Recently, she co-authored a chapter on dysregulation of the Hypothalamic Pituitary Axis during the postpartum period, in *Perinatal and Postpartum Mood Disorders: Perspectives and Treatment Guide for the Health Care Practitioner* (Susan Dowd Stone and Alexis Menkin, 2008). She has a private practice in North Seattle and also works at Country Doctor Community Health Clinic in Seattle. She has served on the Board of Directors for Depression After Delivery (now Postpartum Support International of Washington) and also served as the Telephone Support Coordinator for the PSI of WA Warm Line. She volunteers as a speaker/educator for the Program for Early Parent Support (PEPS of King County) and for Head Start centers in Seattle. She is the mother of three children.

Anna Gruen, MSW was born and raised in Seattle, and earned her MSW and a Graduate Certificate in International Development from the University of Washington. Anna's volunteer and work history has centered in the non-profit world, where she's been committed to supporting immigrant and refugee communities. Anna currently practices social work at Country Doctor Community Health Clinic in Seattle. Anna's work focuses on prenatal and postpartum care with low-income mothers and their families. Anna is honored to carry on the work of her mother, Dawn Gruen, and to contribute to the educational efforts of Postpartum Support International.

Notes:

Notes:

Notes: